P9-AFK-640

THE RELEVANCE OF SCIENCE

C. F. von Weizsäcker

THE RELEVANCE OF SCIENCE

CREATION AND COSMOGONY

GIFFORD LECTURES 1959-60

Harper and Row, Publishers
NEW YORK AND EVANSTON

LIBRARY OF CONGRESS CATALOG CARD NUMBER: 65-11564

Printed in Great Britain
for Harper and Row, Publishers, Inc.

Contents

1	Science and the Modern World	*page* 11
2	Cosmogonical Myths	26
3	Creation in the Old Testament	42
4	Greek Philosophy and Cosmogony	54
5	Christianity and History	77
6	Copernicus, Kepler, Galileo	94
7	Descartes, Newton, Leibniz, Kant	113
8	The Evolution of Life	126
9	Modern Astronomy	141
10	What is Secularization?	157
	A *The concept of secularization*	160
	B *The political revolutions*	164
	C *The Christian background to the modern ambivalence*	166
	D *Belief in progress*	171
	E *Hegel*	173
	F *Marx*	175
	G *The ambivalence of success*	177
	H *What is secularization?*	178
	ACKNOWLEDGEMENTS	184
	INDEX	185

Preface

This book contains the first of the two series of Gifford Lectures which I gave at the University of Glasgow in the years 1959–61. I hope to publish the second series soon. I have retained the lecture form in print in order to maintain for the reader an impression as vivid and as far from a dogmatic assertion of my own views as possible. I also felt that this directness might be better achieved by writing my own English than by having a German text translated; only the tenth lecture is translated from a later German version. Professor R. Gregor Smith has given me invaluable help by reading the complete manuscript and with a cautious hand eliminating impossible English phrases, or at least drawing my attention to what the words I chose really mean in English. I wish to thank Herr H. Holste-Lilie for further corrections of the English text. A German version of these lectures is in course of publication by S. Hirzel in Stuttgart and Zürich.

A reluctant author can be cleverly enticed into writing a book by inviting him to deliver lectures under the condition that they subsequently be published. I feel I should explain in a few sentences what these lectures are intended to be and what they cannot be.

The question posed at the outset, as perhaps the final purpose of these lectures, is pragmatic. I have tried to engage in a dialogue, not so much with the specialists in fields I touch upon, but rather with those intellectuals who sense the dangerous ambivalence of our present-day scientific civilization. I have tried to contribute to the diagnosis of this ambivalence. A diagnosis is a theoretical piece of work with a practical goal—with the some time distant hope of therapy.

The first lecture series attempts this theoretical work in the field of history, namely that history from which our scientific civilization arose. Such an undertaking cannot avoid being philosophy of history. I have only attempted to present a philosophical hypothesis about history; a hypothesis, incidentally, most elements of which are not new. Being a natural scientist by training and still active as such, I have gratefully utilised the results of historical research about the many epochs and people treated in these lectures, insofar as I have been able to assimilate them. The overwhelming amount of material to be assimilated was the main reason for my near insurmountable hesitancy to publish. A guilty conscience towards the better-informed specialist is inevitable, weighing on me constantly.

On the other hand, I have no guilty conscience because of the fact that many historical researchers have an aversion to the philosophy of history altogether. This aversion is well justified when philosophy tries to force its viewpoints dogmatically upon the expert. But philosophy is indispensable when we, who are experts in some fields, want to become aware of our own prejudices. Thus in history every presentation, indeed even each research method, is based on a selection of certain facts considered relevant. But why do we regard these particular facts as relevant? Why do we rely upon certain reports and upon certain self-interpretations and why do we not rely upon others? There is usually unanimous agreement about such questions among members of one scientific school, which means that the philosophy common to a group is no longer felt as a " philosophy ". We do not recognize our own preconceptions as such, and we do not usually diagnose the preconceptions of our adversaries as consequences of different philosophical decisions but as errors. Unconscious philosophy, however, is generally bad philosophy. My objective in these lectures was therefore to make my own philosophical ideas as explicit as possible. I do not maintain that they are absolutely true, but if I am at all to deal with those disquieting questions we have in common, I must of necessity bring up for discussion these philosophical ideas.

At this point another cause for hesitancy appears: the enormity of the philosophical task. Philosophy is necessary but it is too difficult for our human mind; it is necessary nevertheless. Anyone who has observed himself critically has time and again experienced that the successful formulation of a philosophical sentence becomes a stepping-stone, which at once allows and demands that he go beyond it.

I should therefore at least indicate the path upon which I understand this lecture series to be a stepping-stone.

A philosophy of history which propounds theses about the factual course of history challenges us to ask what it means by its use of concepts like history, fact, and understanding—consequently of time, being, and truth. The theses just mentioned appear at first as part of a circular or spiralling movement. So as a guiding question, by means of which I shall trace the history of western thought, I have chosen a problem induced by my work in astrophysics: the history of nature. Human history grew out of the history of nature. Conversely, our present understanding of nature grew out of human history. Thus my earlier lectures on the history of nature form a first semi-circle, which is completed to a full circle by these lectures. Having returned to the starting point, we cannot remain there. The second semi-circle, as " history of the history of nature ", is a reflection upon the first; it proves the contemporary scientist's naïve understanding of nature to be in turn a product of history and compels us to make a second critical round. The second run through the first semi-circle, i.e. the critical analysis of present-day physics, will follow in a second series of lectures, as explained in the last lecture of this present series. A further step, not taken here, would be the reflection upon the basis and essence of this apparently circular movement; that reflection would eventually be part of a philosophy of time, being and truth.

Those who concern themselves with practical efforts towards a therapy of the sickness of our time will be unable to wait until philosophical thinking has completed the winding circles of its reflection. We cannot avoid dealing with both tasks at the same time. Everyone must do this according to his own resources. Anyone neglecting to further his theoretical understanding of our complex world as much as he can, will in the long run do more harm than good in his practical efforts. On the other hand, anyone retreating from the demands of practical work into the tower of pure contemplation will end up with philosophically sterile thoughts.

While the two tasks are certainly related, they are by no means identical, and the techniques appropriate should not be confused. On other occasions I have advanced various opinions on the practical problems of today, and I intend to continue doing so. But these lectures do not terminate in giving practical advice but rather in setting new theoretical tasks. Their contribution to practical life can only consist in the development of our consciousness.

In conclusion I wish to thank the Senators of the University of Glasgow, and especially Sir Hector Hetherington, Principal at that time, for the honour they bestowed upon me by inviting me to be a Gifford lecturer. I would like to express my warmest thanks to all my Glasgow colleagues, students and friends, who received me so well and made my life in Glasgow a great pleasure, even during some gloomy winter months. I am particularly grateful to Professor R. Gregor Smith and his wife for their steady help and encouragement. I cannot end this preface without mentioning the name of the deceased Principal of Aberdeen University, Sir Thomas M. Taylor, who was the first to invite me to Scotland. With him I had many most fruitful discussions on the questions of our times, as related to his ecumenical work. When illness interrupted my lectures, his home afforded me refuge, under the expert care of Lady Taylor. His all-too-early death robbed many people of a counsellor whom they revered and loved, and whom I might have been privileged to call my friend.

C. F. VON WEIZSÄCKER

Hamburg, May 1964

1 *Science and the Modern World*

OUR AGE is an age of science. Speaking about the relevance of science I try to speak about the way in which science succeeds in being the dominating factor of our age. This I do not intend to do by any analysis of sociology, economics or politics. Being trained as a scientist myself, I share the general preconception of scientists that the relevance of science is founded in the truth of science. Hence these lectures will be devoted to the truth of science—to its meaning, its limitations, and its possible ambiguities.

This first series of ten lectures approaches our problem from a historical point of view, and I propose to treat one or two particular problems as examples for a far broader field of questions, a field which would be intractable in its generality.[1] This first lecture is mainly an introduction to the complete series.

Science and the Modern World is the title which one of the few great philosophers of our century gave to his most famous book.[2] In what sense is science characteristic of the modern world?

Our world is a technical world. Such a statement needs no explanation in the age of the radio and the washing machine, in a period in which political history is made by the threat of atomic weapons and by the nimbus of the sputnik. Modern technology, however, would be impossible without modern science. Science and technology may be compared to two neighbouring trees that have sprung out of different seeds and

[1] The second series will offer a philosophical analysis of contemporary physics.
[2] A. N. Whitehead, C.U.P.

still have some separate roots and some separate branches, but whose trunks have grown into one and whose leaves form one huge top. The steam engine of the 18th century was still developed largely out of the traditions of mining and of handicraft; the electromotor of the 19th century would have been impossible without the preceding scientific discoveries of Ampère and Faraday; the nuclear reactor of our century was devised and first built by the atomic physicists themselves. The other side of the medal shows a corresponding picture. I do not need to explain how much natural science in its beginnings owed to the seemingly useless questions asked by the philosophers and to the intellectual methods invented by pure mathematicians, and how little, on the other hand, even the best mind can achieve in modern science if the experimental equipment, made possible by modern technology, is insufficient. In order to express myself simply I shall mostly use the term "science" for this combined structure, this twin tree, of science and technology.

But the relevance of science goes beyond its technical applications. Science seems somehow to represent the character and the fate of our age. I shall try to express this view in two theses which are formulated in a not quite usual terminology; and I shall give the next steps of the analysis in an attempt to interpret these theses. They are:

1. Faith in science plays the rôle of the dominating religion of our time.
2. The relevance of science for our time can, in this moment of history, only be evaluated in terms that express an ambiguity.

Thus religion and ambiguity will be the key concepts of the following passages.

The two theses can only be understood together. Thus in calling faith in science something like the religion of our time I have spoken in ambiguous language. In one sense of the word religion this statement is, I think, true, in another it is certainly wrong. In aiming at an understanding of our time by analysing this ambiguity, I shall first explain in what sense I feel my first thesis can be asserted.

First of all it is certain that our time has no other dominating religion. If you take a European point of view you can rightly say that the dominating religion of the Middle Ages and even of the 19th century was Christianity. The same statement would not apply to our century, for two reasons. First, while Christianity still is the official religion of the majority of the citizens in our western countries, it might be an overstatement to call it dominating. Religious agnosticism is most probably the dominant attitude of the western mind in our times. Secondly, the European point of view is no longer adequate to describe the world which we call our world. While America today shares the European religious tradition, Russia, at least in its dominating class, has left the same tradition; and China, India, the Arab countries, none of which has ever entered this tradition, are most conspicuously members of the world in which we have to live together.

Perhaps we live in a non-religious world. But it is improbable psychologically that the place in the mind of the average human being which in earlier times was filled by religion should now stay empty. My first thesis maintains that this place is now filled by science, or, if you prefer that expression, by scientism, i.e. by faith in science. And I want to go on by stating that the structure of science, looked upon as a factor in the mind of the individual and in society, is such as to enable it to fill that place very efficiently.

What would a sociologist call the indispensable elements of a religion? We may be inclined to mention at least the following three: a common faith, an organized church, and a code of behaviour. Does science provide anything comparable to a faith, a church, and a code of behaviour?

Many admirers of science, it is true, think that science differs from religion in replacing faith by reason. This view, however, seems to be caused by too narrow a concept of faith; or, perhaps, it is precisely an expression of the faith in science. The guiding factor in faith is not belief but trust. Here I use the word belief for the intellectual attitude of an assent which is not knowledge. By trust, on the other hand, I want to indicate a pervading quality of the personality which is not limited to the conscious mind; a quality of reliance which enables us to act precisely in the way in which we ought to act if that in which we trust were clearly before our eyes. It is not primarily the intellectual satisfaction of belief but the moral satisfaction of trust which gives religious faith its strength—here the word "moral" is to be taken in its broadest possible sense. And if you ask what makes the Siamese twins of science and technology the idols of our time, the answer ought to be: it is their trustworthiness. The primitive boy from any village in the world, who knows little about his gods and nothing about science, learns how to tread on the accelerator, and the car will roll. The European Christian and the European agnostic exert their common trust in the technical world, whenever, in entering a room, they push the switch and expect the light to go on. The romantic author who has written a book against the world view of science calls his publisher by telephone because he is late in his proof-reading; and by this very act he tacitly bows before the god whom he defies in his writing. And when the car, the electric light, the telephone fail we do not blame science for being wrong but we blame the individual gadget for being defective, for not corresponding to the standard set by science itself. Such is our faith in science.

But does this trivial trust deserve the name of faith? Is not religious faith revealed from another world, screened in mystery, and confirmed by miracles? Yet the psychological situation of the average man in our time who faces science is just like that of a believer towards his revealed faith. Is not the atom another invisible world and the mathematical formula the sacred text, open before the eye of the initiated whom we call a scientist, and mysterious to the layman? And a miracle was not originally defined as an event which transcends the laws of nature; for the very concept of laws of nature is a modern one. A miracle is a manifestation of superhuman power. The most conspicuous miracles in the history of religious belief were those of feeding, of healing and of destruction; modern agriculture and transportation, modern medicine and modern war machinery work precisely these miracles.

This believing trust in science which, if I have described it rightly, is taking over in our time much of the rôle played by religious faith in earlier ages, I shall call scientism in what follows.

If the religion of science has its faith, does it have a church? Probably you will say: no. Perhaps the Communist Party tries to be something like such a church. But then it is not more than a very powerful sect. The majority of the believers in science in the world of this day do not share the communist interpretation of science; they feel that much of what communists call science is not science at all. But, strangely enough, though there is no church of science, there is a priesthood of science: the scientists themselves. I have called them the initiated. It is their understanding of a common truth by which they recognize each other. That physics is science and dialectical materialism is not, for example, became clear, in 1955 at the first Geneva conference on the peaceful use of atomic energy. There many western and Soviet physicists met for the first time, and a good deal of classified information was made public. It was a great experience to see that the numerical values of the same atomic constants, measured in deep secrecy in different countries under opposed political systems and creeds, when compared, turned out to be identical down to the last decimal. Nothing of the sort happened with respect to theories on society. The Soviet physicist and his colleague from the West are united by a bond which no political dissension can touch; they are united by a common truth.

Let me make a remark about priests and truth. Sceptics have invented the theory that the higher clergy of a religious community cannot possibly believe their own dogmas and miracle-stories. The sceptic, seeing that priests on higher levels are usually clever, cannot imagine that they should believe what in his eyes is nonsense. He may be right concerning the minor hocus-pocus that seems to be inevitable in religion as well as in medicine. He is most certainly wrong, though, about the basic creed. The priest is the man who understands the creed and who is able to explain it as far as it can be explained to the uninitiated. The priest has taken the longer path along which the meaning of the scriptures is opened step by step. He takes it and knows how to lead others along it. The priests of the same religion, whatever may be their personal differences, are united by the common possession of what they most firmly believe to be truth. Just for this reason differences in the interpretation of this truth which seem trifling from outside are of such importance to those within. And now the scientists find themselves in the possession of such a truth which unites them in their own eyes as well as in the eyes of the world. They are forced into a priest-like position, whether they like it or not.

As a third element of religion I mentioned its code of behaviour. This includes a moral code. But many religions have a particular ritual code besides. Historically the concept of pure ethics is probably a rather late stage in the development of a religion. In the earliest codes we usually find moral rules embedded in ritual. Ritual contains the rules of right behaviour towards those superhuman powers on which we depend all our life. These rules are generally incomprehensible to modern man. He is no longer able to produce within himself, even in a playful manner, the state of mind of a person who truly believes in the reality of those powers. He would find a very good analogy, though, in his own belief in the laws of nature and in his readiness to obey the directions for use which are attached to any piece of modern machinery. The car does not run; of course, you forgot to release the hand-brake. If you don't learn to use the right pedal you will never be able to drive a car. If you don't learn to spell the right formula at the right moment, the demons will never obey your will.

Ethics grows out of ritual as right behaviour towards our fellow man grows out of right behaviour towards the invisible powers. In its peculiar way, the technical world knows this transition, too, and it is vital for our future that we should understand it. If you know how to work the knobs you will be able to drive a car at 60 mph. But if you try to drive your car at 60 mph through a city street, you are violating the traffic law; more than that, you are reckless, and you know it. There is an inherent ethics of the technical world, but it is not yet well understood. To do everything that is technically feasible, is non-technical behaviour; it is not, as some believe, technical *avant-gardism*, but it is childish. The little boy tries out his toy without thinking of the furniture and of the peace of mind of his parents; the adult uses technical apparatus as means to an end. I feel that this consideration applies even to such great problems as weapons and war in an atomic age. Much that is done technically in our time is in no way better than black magic. It is not worthy of a mature technical age. We still live more in a time of technical ritual than of technical ethics.

Let us now take a step back. I have tried to draw a picture of the relevance of science in modern life by comparing it to a religion. I suppose that some of you will have felt rising within your minds a strong objection. Is this comparison between science and religion anything but blasphemy? I am not here speaking of those believers in science who would object to my comparison because they think science to be true and religion to be wrong; their case will be treated at length in later lectures. In speaking of blasphemy I want to express the opposite feeling, that of the truly religious man or woman who will say: whatever analogy there may be between the public influence of science and that of religion, still science is not religion and should never be allowed to take its place. I fully agree with them. The reason for my using such ambiguous language will become clearer in the further course of these lectures, too. As a first step I shall now turn the tables and try to give a few arguments which can be used against scientism as a religion of our age. I shall first speak about the success and failure of scientism, then about its meaning, and this will lead me to the question of its origin.

Even if we speak of scientism as a dominating religion we must ask if it is a true view of life. And we should not be inclined to call it true if it leads into catastrophe or even into a life not worthy of human beings. Therefore I think the question of success is relevant. What does our experience teach us about the success or failure of science and of scientism? I think the answer cannot but be ambiguous. Science has led us into a two-edged, an ambiguous situation. Any example, if we are not afraid of thinking through its consequences, will make that obvious.

Medicine and hygiene have saved thousands of millions of lives. This is the most wonderful success science can boast of. Death has not been conquered, it is true, and will not be conquered. To save lives means to save them for a while; such is our human condition. We cannot want more than to save the lives of children so that they may see maturity, and the lives of adults so that they may fulfil their calling and, as is said of Abraham, may die in a good old age, full of years (Gen. 35, 8). Hence it means a great deal to raise the life expectation of the new-born from thirty-five to sixty-five years.

But another aspect of this success is the enormous increase of the world population. It has more than doubled within one century, and no limit seems as yet to be approached. How can we feed the human beings whom we condemn to life by our medicine? Is not Malthus right after all?

I see just two solutions to this problem, a preliminary one and a final one. The preliminary answer is industrialization and intensification of agriculture, combined with an unfettered exchange of goods all over the earth; this answer, to put it briefly, is an increase in food production. But the area of our planet is limited; finally the increase of population must come to an end. If we do not want to rely on a break-down of our civilization I see no final answer but general birth control.

Both solutions rest on certain political conditions. The later we stop the population increase the greater will be the number of people to be fed. The greater this number the more complicated and hence the more vulnerable is the system of technology and of organization needed to feed them. The classical concept of the sovereignty of nations which includes the freedom to wage war becomes increasingly incompatible with the functioning of this system. It becomes more and more evident that war must be abolished. Yet how shall we enforce peace? War is an institution as old as human history. If science forces us to abolish war it strains our inventiveness and our good will to the utmost. Can we assert that mankind will be equal to such an enormous task?

Probably more than peace will be enforced. Can we rely on voluntary birth control? I was present at a meeting of scientists where this problem was treated. A representative of Communist China, a very nice man by the way, rose to say: "The problem must look insoluble to a capitalist society. To us it is no problem. In China we have now 615 million people. Within the next 15 years we will go on to 800 million. Then we will stop." He spoke and sat down. Here a totalitarian sect of scientism offers its solution to a problem created by science. Is a world dominated by science compatible with human freedom? I am not going to answer this question, but I think we are compelled to raise it.

What contribution has science so far given to the solution of international political problems? I am afraid, the most conspicuous contributions in our time are guided missiles and atomic bombs. I do not deny that just by transforming war into an all-out catastrophe these weapons may contribute to the preservation of peace in our time. Such is the ambiguity of the effects of science: medicine, made to save lives, creates the nearly insurmountable problem of population increase; weapons, made to kill lives, seem to contribute to the establishment of peace. But if the inherent dialectic of these effects turns black into white once, is there a guarantee that it will not turn white into black again? Are we prepared to organize that peace which weapons can make imperative without making it possible at the same time?

These lectures are not intended to offer solutions for our problems but to make a step towards an investigation into their roots. They are not concerned with therapy but only with diagnosis. I am afraid many proposed therapeutical measures have failed or are bound to fail because they rest on an insufficient analysis of the situation, on an insufficient diagnosis. Diagnostics need infinite patience of investigation and they need an eye for the inconspicuous symptoms, for the hidden causes of great effects. Thus let me try to indicate some less conspicuous problems to which an analysis of those already mentioned may lead us. The contribution of science to the organization of peace will to a large extent consist in planning. Planning will be possible and necessary in international affairs, in economy, in social structure, in health, education, and many other things. Planning is inevitable in a scientific world like ours. But certainly it is easier to plan a machine than to plan the behaviour of certain human beings who like to exert their free wills. Hence it is easier to plan their behaviour if we try to treat them as though they were machines. Servitude is more easily planned than freedom. It is true, if we do not open our common life to the spirit of scientific planning, we will see chaos. But if we do open it to that spirit, we will have to withstand the temptation of planning away our humanity, of bringing a servitude over us, the more dangerous the less visibly it enters our communities.

No well-established servitude rests mainly on brute physical force. It rests on a domination of minds. I lived under a dictatorship for twelve years. I did not behave like a hero, but I studied the functioning of the system. Perhaps the main weakness of that particular dictatorship was that it did not believe in science; still it knew how to apply the means provided by science. For example it has led me to believe to this day that the radio contains a more deep-rooted danger than modern weapons do. Weapons are useless if people are not prepared to use them; propaganda is one of the main methods to prepare them for their use. Perhaps one may dare to go a step further. An integrated personality may be able to resist propaganda. Yet the habit of hearing the radio not for what it brings to the conscious mind but as a placating or titillating background-noise may do more than we know towards a disintegration of the subconscious mind. What demons obsess our technology to make that contemplation impossible to which we ought to return from time to time if we want to find the right use of technology itself?

Human nature is not free from the danger of self-destruction. Science has not created this danger but it brings it into the foreground of the scene. A psychologist may be tempted to call it a positive tendency towards the destruction of our own ends. Take another example. Precisely because we have invented so many instruments for saving time we are all haunted by lack of time. Once such an effect is seen its causality is easily understood. The number of people we can reach by railway, motor-car, aeroplane, and telephone is so much greater than the number with which communication was possible in earlier times that this increase by far surpasses the gain of time in every single human contact. But this is an explanation *ex eventu*. Will we learn to overcome the effect which we have been unable to forestall or even to foresee?

Science, it seems, is a two-edged sword. No optimism or pessimism seems to be adequate if we want to describe what it has given us and what it promises for the future. Science is still growing. Every effect which we see now can be superseded by a greater one. Whether the greater effect will be better or worse than the one we know is difficult to guess. Therefore I have chosen the word ambiguity to describe what we know about the success of science so far.

Let us go on and say that the meaning of scientism is as ambiguous as the effects of science. If science plays the rôle of a religion, we may rightly ask two questions: What does it know about God? and: What does it know about man?

I propose to postpone the first question. It is true when I called scientism a religion I exposed myself to the objection that religions worship gods or God, while science does not speak of a god. But there are religious systems like original Buddhism or Confucianism which we might call atheistic, and science, on the other hand, believes in powers and laws which would have been called divine by many people in the past; a more thorough study of historic religion which I hope to give in these lectures ought to precede an answer. But we need no preparation for asking the second question: What does science know about man?

Let me explain the case by a well-known silly little story. A man is found at night searching every inch of the street in the light-cone of a street lamp. He explains: "I have lost my door-key." "Are you sure you have lost it under the lamp?" "No." "Why, then, do you look for it there?" "Because here at least I can see." Science cannot select the order in which it wants to treat its subjects according to their importance for human life. The motion of the planets is not relevant to human happiness or salvation. But it turned out to be a comparatively simple problem for mathematical treatment, and thus through the efforts of Copernicus, Kepler, and Newton its theory became the keystone of modern science. Human nature is less simple. Human actions will most probably never be predicted with mathematical exactness. Even if we accept the comparison of the human brain to electronic calculating machines, we have to admit that the biggest electronic brains have so far only reached the same degree of complication as the central nervous system of an earth-worm. I am afraid the scientist who offers to explain human nature is at least far ahead of his time.

But the key we seem to have lost is just the key to human nature. Religion has at all times claimed to possess this key. Even the agnostic who doubts the claim as raised by religion will probably have to admit that it would be vital for us to have an adequate understanding of human nature. All the troubles I mentioned before do not arise out of an insufficient mastery of the powers of the physical world; they arise out of our inability to conduct, to predict or even to understand the actions of human beings. Now to deny that science makes important contributions to such an understanding would again be wrong. But besides admitting the limitations of our scientific knowledge of the human heart we have to understand the highly ambiguous potentialities of the power implied in such a knowledge. The idea that the psychological insight of a Freud might be combined in one man with the purposes and the cunning of a Goebbels, will make us shudder. Pavlov's study of conditioned reflexes seems to be the historical origin of the method now called brain-washing. Scientific knowledge means power. Power ought to mean responsibility. But that scientific knowledge would supply us with the ethical greatness needed to bear this responsibility is a hope not warranted by the facts. I think it can be stated bluntly that scientism, if it rests its trust on the expectation that science by its own nature is enabled to give us sufficient guidance in human affairs, is a false religion. Its faith, if going so far, is superstition; the rôle of the priest does not become the scientist, and good scientists know that; the scientific code of behaviour needs a background of an ethics which science has not been able to provide.

But this statement is negative and hence insufficient. Our next step will be the question: how did science come to play the ambiguous rôle in which we find it today?

With this question I have reached the subject matter of this first series of lectures. I can now describe them as lectures on the historical origin of scientism. This is to be their modest contribution to the diagnosis we are searching for. But for a thorough investigation even this question is still too far-fetched. As I said in the beginning, I shall select one particular problem by which the origin of scientism may be illustrated. I choose a problem which is far from any technical application but close to the scientific concerns of the first centuries of our modern era. It is the problem of the relationship between the two concepts of creation and of cosmogony. I shall use the rest of this hour for a brief exposition of the problem.

In 1692 Richard Bentley the philologist, then a young man, delivered his famous Boyle Sermons in London. With great intellectual splendour, which cannot but touch the modern reader as somewhat haughty, he sets out to refute atheism. His argument culminates in the following proof for the existence of God: Our great scientist, Isaac Newton, has shown that the motion of the planets in their orbits can be explained by the laws of nature, i.e. by the axioms of dynamics and the law of gravity. But these laws which explain how the planetary system is functioning since it came into being, cannot explain its origin. Hence the origin of the system can only be understood as due to the design of an intelligent Maker.

Contracting Bentley's argument into one sentence one might say: there is no scientific cosmogony, and therefore there must have been creation. In a classical manner the argument opposes the two ideas of creation and of cosmogony, and induces us to understand them as representing two similarly opposed general tendencies: a religious and a scientific explanation of the world. Its admirers certainly considered the argument to be particularly stringent because it gave science its recognized place within the religious explanation: it was just Newton's success in deducing the actual motions of the planets which transformed his failure to explain the origin of the system from a mere admission of ignorance into a positive argument for a divine Maker.

In the following lectures I hope to prove, however, that by opposing the two explanations in such a manner the religious interpretation of the world had already made its own defeat inevitable. Either Bentley's starting point is wrong or religion has lost its case. In 1755, sixty-three years after Bentley's sermons, the young Immanuel Kant, later to become more famous as a philosopher, published his *Theory of the Heavens* in which he gave an acceptable mechanical explanation of the origin of our planetary system. The gap in science which should have proved God was closed. Another fifty years later the famous astronomer Pierre Simon de Laplace invented a similar theory independently of Kant. There is an anecdote that Napoleon asked him where in his theory there was a place left for God; and that he replied: "*Sire, je n'avais pas besoin de cette hypothèse-là.*"

Kant himself considered and rejected the possible atheistic implications of his theory. In order to be able to do so he had to reject Bentley's argument. He felt that a God who framed the laws of nature in such a way as to lead to the necessary formation of planetary systems was more to be admired than a God who first created mechanical laws and then had to violate them in order to make a world. How can you speak of the works of blind mechanical necessity as opposed to the works of Divine Reason, if, being a Christian, you believe in a God who created everything, including the laws of mechanics?

Kant was not sufficiently trained as a historian of philosophy and theology; else he would have realized that these two opposed interpretations of God's work have their origin in the two roots of the traditional Christian views about creation: in Plato's *Timaeus* and in the Old Testament. Plato describes the Maker of the Universe as ordering by the light of reason a dark world of blind mechanical necessity which did not depend on him for its chaotic pre-existence. In the Old Testament, on the other hand, God made everything, light and darkness, order and necessity, soul and body. Perhaps Kant's view is closer to the Bible than Bentley's, although both of them, compared with either Plato or the Bible, are definitely modern. I propose to treat in detail the original meaning of both the Platonic and the biblical view, their merging in Christianity and their modern transformation.

In order to do so we must start even before Plato and the Bible. To the believer in scientism, the story of creation, both in Plato's and in the Bible's form, is just a myth. Mythology, in his view, is opposed to reason; the two Greek words, *mythos* and *logos*, are often used to describe this contraposition. If, however, we want to understand these two roots of the Christian theology of creation adequately we must go further back by one step. We must compare them with real mythology in order to see in what degree they themselves already belong to the world of reason.

This outline of the problem should suffice to illustrate the plan for the following lectures. One lecture will be devoted to true mythology; three lectures will consider the views on the origin of the world in the Old Testament, in Greek philosophy, and in Christian theology; two lectures will investigate the origin of the problem raised by modern science from the 16th to the 18th century; two lectures will describe the cosmogony accepted by the science of our century; and the last of this first series of lectures will return to the question of the first one: science and the modern world; it will do so under the particular aspect of the secularization of Christian faith.

2 *Cosmogonical Myths*

MODERN SCIENCE seems to expose the concept of creation as a myth. In this second lecture I want to study what cosmogonical myths really are. Let me begin by considering the meaning of the words "cosmogonical myth".

The Greek word *kosmos* means order, ornament, and beauty. The Pythagorean philosophers made it mean the world which is of perfect beauty because it is ordered. In the Christian tradition it comes to mean the world as distinct from God. The final syllables—*gonical*—are derived from the Greek root—*gen*—which indicates birth and more generally every way of coming into being, every becoming. Cosmogony then is, objectively speaking, the way in which the world came into being, or it is, subjectively speaking, the teaching about this way.

The Greek word *mythos* originally means nothing but word or speech. In a narrower sense it means a story told. At all times people asked: Who were our forefathers? Who gave us bread, tools and weapons? Whence came birth and death? Whence came Heaven and Earth? As an answer they are told a story. This story is a *mythos*, a myth.

I should like to read to you a genuine cosmogonical myth in full. But that would take me not much less than an hour for reading and another hour or two for explaining. Instead I want to use the first half of this lecture in indicating briefly the contents of three relevant cosmogonical myths, and the second half in discussing their meaning. I choose a Babylonian myth, a Greek myth and a Scandinavian one.

The Babylonian *Epic of Creation* was written by men who lived as many years before Christ as we live after Christ; it will become relevant for our interpretation of the Old Testament, for there can be no doubt that the author of Genesis I knew it and despised it. The Greek *Theogony* as told by Hesiod was known to every Greek philosopher; Plato was certainly convinced that he had done better than Hesiod when he had written his *Timaeus*. The verses and tales of the Icelandic *Edda* were written down less than one thousand years ago; they may give us at least some hint on the views of our own medieval ancestors before, by being baptized, they were exposed to the tradition of the ancient world.

When on high the heavens were not named,
And beneath a home bore no name,
And Apsû primeval, their engenderer,
And the Form, Tiâmat, the bearer of all of them,
There mingled their waters together;

Dark chambers were not built, and marshlands were not seen;
When none of the gods had been brought into being,
And they were not named, and fates were not fixed:
Then were created the gods in the midst thereof;
Lahmu and Lahamu were brought into being and were named.
For ages they grew up and became lofty.
Ansar and Kisar were created more excellent than they.
The days lengthened themselves and the years increased.
Anu their son, the rival of his fathers,
Ansar made Anu his first-born equal to himself,
And as to Anu he begat Nudimuned his equal . . .

Thus, in S. Langdon's translation,[1] begins the long ritual song which was sung every year in springtime in ancient Babylon at the New Year festival. It is a document of the same great period of Mesopotamian culture as Hammurabi's book of law; but it was still in use 1500 years later, in the time of Alexander the Great. The text which we possess was found in the library of the Assyrian king Assurbanipal, who lived in the 7th century BC.

You do not need to remember the perplexing abundance of divine names which are here solemnly introduced. But then a drama develops and I repeat those names which are important as *dramatis personae*.

Apsû and Tiâmat are primeval waters. Apsû is known as the ocean of fresh water stretching beneath the earth, from which springs and wells are supplied. Tiâmat is the salt-water ocean. Here they are man and woman, engenderer and bearer of everything to come. Of the long generations of gods deriving from them the younger ones were the great gods of the Babylonians. Anu, the last but one in the above quotation, is the Lord of Heaven in Babylonian religion. Nudimuned "whom he begat his equal", is another name of Ea, the Ruler of the Sea.

A deadly conflict arises between the eldest couple Apsû and

[1] *The Babylonian Epic of Creation*, Clarendon Press 1923.

Tiâmat and their offspring. "The brothers, the gods ... troubled the thoughts of Tiâmat with singing in the midst of their abode." Apsû says to Tiâmat:

> Their way has become grievous to me.
> By day I am rested not, by night I sleep not.
> I will destroy them and confound their ways.
> Let tranquillity reign, and let us sleep, even us.

But this first fight is won by the younger gods. Ea, the young god, "the exceedingly wise, the clever in skill", bewitches Apsû and slays him in his sleep. Then he "fixes upon Apsû his dwelling". The slain body of Apsû becomes the palace of his killer. And this is consistent, since Apsû is the Water and Ea is the Lord of the Waters.

Only in this moment is the hero of the poem born. He is Marduk, the city-god of Babylon, the god of spring, of the sun and of the thunderstorm, greater than all the elder gods.

But Tiâmat prepares her revenge. She, the Mother of the Depth, the dragon of the sea, now gives birth to monsters; with poison-like blood she fills their bodies. Here are some of them: the Viper, the Raging Serpent, the Great Lion, the Gruesome Hound, the Scorpion-man, the Spirits of Wrath, the Fish-man and the Fish-ram.

In deep horror the younger gods transfer the dominion to Marduk who alone can save them. Armed with lightning he goes to war.

> He made a net to enfold the belly of Tiâmat,
> He caused the four winds to come under control that nothing of her might escape ...
> He created the evil wind, the Tempest, the Hurricane,
> The Fourfold-wind, the Sevenfold-wind, the Devastating-wind, the Unrivalled-wind.

The raging winds filled Tiâmat's belly, and Marduk let loose an arrow ... it rent asunder her heart; he bound her and quenched her breath of life.

Now, when the struggle of the gods has come to an end,

Marduk creates the world. He makes it out of the corpse of Tiâmat.

> He split her into two parts, like an oyster.
> Half of her he set up and made the heavens as a covering.
> The lord measured the dimension of Apsû.
> A vast abode its counterpart he fixed—even the Earth.

In the very last scene man is made. Perhaps a lost part of the poem has told that some service has weighed too heavily on the gods. Now a god, Kingu, who had been Tiâmat's general, is killed.

> With his blood Ea made mankind
> In the cult service of the gods, and he set the gods free.[1]

And men build a city as a dwelling for Marduk, they build Babylon. At the end all the gods assemble and sing Marduk's praise, calling his fifty names.

So much about Babylon. I shall speak more briefly of Greece and Iceland.

Hesiod says in his *Theogony*:

> Verily at the first Chaos came to be, but next wide-bosomed Earth, the ever-sure foundation of all the deathless ones who hold the peaks of snowy Olympus and dim Tartarus in the depth of the wide pathed Earth, and Eros, fairest among the deathless gods . . . From Chaos came forth Erebus and black Night; but of Night were born Aether and Day . . . And Earth first bore starry Heaven, equal to herself, to cover her on every side, and to be an ever-sure abiding-place for the blessed gods.[2]

To Heaven, Earth bore many powerful and terrifying divine children. But Heaven "used to hide them all away in a secret place so soon as each was born, and would not suffer them to come up into the light; and Heaven rejoiced in his evil doing. But vast Earth groaned within, being straitened, and she thought of a crafty and an evil wile." She forms a great sickle, and Cronos,

[1] Langdon, *op. cit.*
[2] Translation by H. G. Evelyn-White, Heinemann.

her youngest son, vindicates her; when Heaven comes again, "bringing on night and longing for love", Cronos emasculates his own father. Thus Heaven and Earth are separated.

Cronos now is Lord of the World. Fearing that his children will do to him as he did to his father, he devours them as soon as they are born. Zeus, the youngest, is cunningly saved, and when he is grown up he dethrones his father. Defending his rule against the Titans, his father's elder brothers, with his weapon, the thunderbolt, he establishes the dominion of the Olympian Gods, a dominion which lasts to this day.

About the origin of man the Greeks told different stories. According to Hesiod "the deathless gods who dwell on Olympus" created five successive generations of men: men of the golden, the silver, the bronze age, the heroes and, fifth, our own age of iron. Others tell that the Titan Prometheus formed men out of clay and that for them he stole the fire from heaven. I shall not expand on these well-known classical myths.

Scandinavian seafarers who settled in Iceland wrote in the *Edda*:

> Twas the earliest of times when Ymir lived;
> then was sand nor sea nor cooling wave,
> nor was Earth found ever, nor Heaven on high,
> there was Yawning of Deeps and nowhere grass.[1]

The Younger Edda explains this, trivializing it a little. The Yawning of Deeps, Ginungagap in Old Norse, is a valley between the ice of Niflheim and the burning heat of Muspilheim:

> Ginungagap was as warm and mild as windless air. And when the heat blasts from Muspilheim met the rime, so that it melted into drops, then, by the might of him who sent the heat, the drops quickened into life and took the likeness of a man who got the name Ymir . . . Evil was he and all his offspring . . . It is said that when he slept he fell into a sweat, and then there grew under his left arm a man and a woman,

[1] *The Elder or Poetic Edda*, translation by Olive Bray, 1908.

> and one of his feet begat with the other a son. From these come the races that are called frost-giants.[1]

Then the melting rime formed into a cow whose milk streams fed Ymir. And the cow

> licked the salt-stones that were covered with rime, and the first day that she licked the stones there came out of them in the evening a man's hair, the second day a man's head, and the third day the whole man was there. This man's name was Buri; he was fair of face, great and mighty, and he begat a son whose name was Bor. This Bor married a woman whose name was Bestla, the daughter of the giant Bolthorn. They had three sons: Odin, Vili and Ve. And it is my belief that this Odin and his brothers are the rulers of heaven and earth.[2]

Bor's sons slay Ymir, and in his blood they drown the whole race of frost-giants, except one who escapes. Then they make heaven and earth:

> From the flesh of Ymir the world was formed,
> from his blood the billows of the sea,
> the hills from his bones the trees from his hair
> the sphere of heaven from his skull.
>
> Out of his brows the blithe Powers made
> Midgarth for sons of men,
> and out of his brains were the angry clouds
> all shaped above in the sky.[3]

In other strophes the *Edda* tells how the three gods Odin, Hönir and Lodur made man and woman out of an ash-tree and an elm-tree which they had found, fateless, at the shore of the sea, by giving them life and soul.

Such are the tales. What is their meaning?

He who asks such a question is no longer a child of the mythical

[1] *The Younger Edda*, translation by Rasmus Anderson, 1880.
[2] Anderson, *op. cit.* [3] Bray, *op. cit.*

age; else the myths would tell him what they want to tell, without an explanation. Think of their little brothers, the fairy-tales. The youngster who asks what the fairy-tales mean has outgrown the age of fairy-tales. If, then, he should still wish to understand them, he must outgrow that age, too, in which he is proud of not believing in fairy-tales. Our situation with respect to the myths is very similar.

What are the myths? You can compare them to fairy-tales, but they contain another kind of greatness, of horror, of sanctity. Should we call them the great poems of the prehistoric age?

At least the free play of fancy seems to be common to myths and to poetry. Freely those myth-tellers invent generations of gods who live and act in a world like ours although they existed before heaven and earth were made and although they did deeds beyond every human measure. Here a god eats his children, there a sly old peasant thinks up the idea of a cow which licked the first man out of the ice. From a slain corpse the world is built, and nobody asks on what soil it rests. But as in poetry the imagination of the myth-teller is bound by laws of form. Poetry is older than prose; the first mythical texts are poems obeying rigid formal rules. Here liturgy would be a better comparison than our modern subjective poetry. Absolute strictness of form facilitates the oral tradition and implies the sanctity of the text. Even our children want to hear the same tales told in ever the same words.

Yet even the contents of the three myths I told you is far more strictly determined than may appear at first sight. The wild and delicate play of fancy is but an adornment, while in fact the three narrators seem to see and to tell the very same things. There is a beginning which nearly evades description by human words. Then we see an elemental power, dark or cold: water, earth, ice. Out of it bright, heavenly forces arise. They appear in human shape, they are gods. Strife arises between the old and the young divine powers, and the younger gods are victorious. The ruling god of our aeon makes men; in two of our three tales he first makes heaven and earth out of the slain body of the enemy.

Where do these correspondences come from? Certainly myths have migrated. But why have people been prepared to accept foreign myths and to retell them as their own? I want to maintain that these cosmogonical myths contain a common rational structure, a kind of philosophy. This philosophy, I think, is so reasonable that it should not surprise us to find it invented independently by different nations and even less to find it accepted when told by travellers. But it should be clear from the outset that this comparison of myths with philosophy is to be taken even less literally than their comparison with fairy-tales, poetry, or liturgy. A myth cannot be fully transformed into a system of unambiguous concepts. We, children of a later age, cannot understand a myth without tentatively applying our categories to it. It contains elements corresponding to all of them, identical with none of them. Thus our categories dissect the myth into incoherent aspects, and a true understanding of the myth, if we ever can reach it, must finally let these aspects disappear again in an integral body.

What, then, is the philosophical aspect of our myths? Philosophy means that we reflect on our own presuppositions. Philosophy would not tell a tale but ask how the tale can be meaningful; how it can be a possible tale. Let us ask this question by reversing the time-sequence of the tale.

Here we are, human beings in a world whose frame is heaven and earth. Where do we come from, whence came heaven and earth? We know only one way how such wonderful and incomprehensible works can have arisen: somebody must have made them.

He who is to make such things must be able to reason as a man, but he must be immensely more powerful. Yet such beings, similar to mankind but immensely more mighty, were known to all the ancient nations: Who, living in such a nation, would not know the gods? I am not yet asking what gods are. I now take them as self-evidently known as they were in those times.

Everything made is made out of some material: bread from grain, weapons from metal, statues of the gods from burned clay, stone or brass. In the same way the gods have made us from the materials of their world. The gods, too, have a world and a history.

But does not this lead us into an infinite regression? If the gods live in their world like men, whence did the gods come, whence came their world?

The younger gods can be distinguished from the world that surrounds them. But in the beginning of the genealogies of gods we find beings that appear like acting and speaking persons as well as like elements of the primeval cosmic landscape. Apsû is the ocean. He is slain by his offspring Ea. Then Ea makes his dwelling on Apsû. The slain god is now the palace of his killer. If Apsû was the ocean, Ea can be distinguished from the ocean, being the lord of the ocean.

The god who is identical with his element is the earlier stage. The younger gods who can be distinguished from the element in which they rule are more man-like; and they are the gods who made heaven and earth, who made man and guarantee the world-order in which we live. Implicit in the distinction of the generations of gods is the idea that the material of the world is older than its present order. The god who gave it the order can be distinguished from his work precisely because of this order, while the shapeless original material is in an obscure way element and god alike.

But how could order ever arise out of primeval indistinction? By their very nature the first gods were no artisans who would have made a thing according to a plan. They could only bear order as a mother bears her child; she gives rise to what is different from her by a necessity beyond any will. Only an accidental effect like the licking of the divine cow offers an alternative, and this one seems to be a late invention. But the new world of order disturbs the quiet and the power of its ancestors: the elder gods fear and hate their children. They must be slain by their children; only then their dead body becomes the material from which a world of order can be built.

Have we understood the origin of the gods and their world? The first gods were gods and world in one. But whence did they come?

Somehow even earlier than the first gods there was a state which we now like to call by its Hesiodic name Chaos. But Chaos does not just mean disorder, because then there would at least exist something. Literally chaos means yawning. The same word appears in the *Edda*: Ginungagap is yawning of the deeps. This state can only be described by negations. None of the things that make our world were there: neither heaven nor earth, neither grass nor sea, neither name nor fate. If you want to describe an absolute beginning you cannot do it otherwise. It could not be the beginning if it contained anything that still might have an origin. The beginning must be a kind of nothingness; but since it is the beginning of something it must have some part in being. Let us call it nothingness pregnant with being.

The very first idea in the texts is usually a determination of time: "When on high the heavens were not named"; "Verily at the first . . ."; "'Twas the earliest of times." Since this time is the time of the beginning you cannot assign it a definite moment or a definite duration, both of which would presuppose form and limits. The first time is as much and as little time as Chaos has turned out to be being.

This, I think, is the implicit philosophy of the cosmogonical myths. Has later philosophical speculation had any important idea to add? Leaving the material questions to later lectures we may say now: at least it added explicitness. This philosophy which we extracted from a told tale may have been present in it in the same way in which logic is present in the living speech of an intelligent person who never studied logic; the narrator who was far from possessing this philosophy explicitly would at least have felt an irritation whenever his tale violated it. Let us say that this philosophy is implicit in the myth. Hence the myth is at the same time explained and distorted by our explicit philosophical interpretation. Let us return to a more integral understanding of the myth.

The aspects which I mentioned before, as fairy-tale, poetry, liturgy, philosophy, are aspects of the form of presentation and reasoning. There are different aspects of the matter, too, of which the myths speak. So far we have only interpreted them as cosmogony, this word understood in its seemingly plain sense. But we had to defer a central question: the question what the gods mean. This question will open aspects quite different from what we consider to be cosmogony.

Let there be no doubt: in asking what the gods mean we are as hopelessly naive as the boy who is proud that he no longer believes in fairy tales. To a man who believes in a god the god exists and the question what the god means is meaningless to him. If understanding a person means to be able to feel what the other person feels, an adequate understanding of religion would imply the question, not what gods mean but what gods are. This is just what our proud boy, scientism, does not want to admit. But let us not overstrain our powers. We cannot restore a lost faith by our will, and the faith in the gods of these myths is lost to us, whatever we may think of religion. Hence let us ask the only question within our present reach, and that is the question what these gods mean. Only let us not be satisfied by our own answers. Let them not keep us from further questioning.

Many of the gods evidently represent powers of nature. Marduk and Zeus are lords of the lightning and of the thunderstorm. Tiâmat is the water, Ymir is the ice. The victory of Marduk's winds over Tiâmat's water-monsters is the ever recurring victory of spring over winter; it is not accidental that the epic was sung every new year in spring. In that sense, however, the epic does not seem to be cosmogonical. It rather seems to celebrate a recurring event. I shall come back to this question soon.

The gods do not only represent powers of nature. They also represent political powers. And, strangely enough, the same god can show both aspects. Marduk is the city-god of Babylon. The younger gods were only able to resist Tiâmat after having chosen the youngest offspring, even Marduk, to be their ruler. His elevation above the other gods in turn elevates Babylon above the other cities of Mesopotamia. In older forms of the myth Enlil, the god of Nippur, was the hero of the tale; still other gods seem to have played the same rôle at other times and in other places. The Assyrians, who seem to have excelled in the military field more than in poetry, took over the Babylonian text, only replacing the name of Marduk throughout the poem by the name of their national god Assur; in this form most of the text has come down to us from Assurbanipal's library. In each of these forms the myth celebrates some political act which, because of the sacred nature of the political bodies of that time, was at the same time a religious one. The victory of a town or of a nation was a victory of its gods. Perhaps the changing dynasties of gods reflect some changes of human dynasties, too.

Finally, the modern psychology of the subconscious mind, especially as presented by C. G. Jung, opens up quite a different understanding of the gods. To it the image of the god is a sign visible to the conscious mind but representing a far deeper reality in the soul. Let us try to interpret our myths as strictly as possible according to this understanding. Their drama of theogony then is really a drama of psychogony, of the becoming of the soul. In his representations of the becoming of the world then, man is projecting the powers that act in himself; he thus tries to see himself in objectivation. But the god is always more than the image that I paint of him. This is expressed clearly in the myth, saying that the gods made man, not vice versa. My consciousness is not the lord of those deeper realities in my soul that emerge in the images of the gods, but it springs from them, rests upon them and depends on them. In the depth of our souls is the battle of the gods. The shapeless dark powers of the unconscious are older than the powers of light and order, and they hate that order. Tiâmat is the water, and the water is well known by psychologists to mean the unconscious. Within our own soul the principle of light has to slay the principle of darkness if order is to be built. Even the firm soil on which we stand is still surrounded by "deep-swirling Okeanos". Who, if he ever has learnt to know himself, will not recognize himself in this image?

Of the three interpretations of the gods which I have mentioned—the physical, the political and the psychological interpretation—I think the last one comes closest to answering the question what the gods really are. It penetrates most deeply into the origin of the immense power gods have always exerted on mankind; a power of which physical forces seem to be just a likeness and from which political dominions derive their very strength. For there is but one power I can never escape: the power of a voice speaking within myself.

Yet the psychological interpretation is just an aspect or an approximation. It cannot be the final answer, for two reasons. Firstly, it describes the reality of the gods in more or less atheistic language. Secondly, it still dissects the unity of mythical thought, taking out one aspect. The two shortcomings are interlinked, and they have their common origin in a way of thought which is still too naively modern. I shall try to explain both points.

It describes the reality of the gods in a more or less atheistic language. I say "more or less", because the meaning of the language used depends to some extent on the speaker. In any case, the term "psychological" is apt to transform the gods into something merely subjective. This little word "merely" may undo the understanding of the gods which was reached in saying that we depend on them since they created us and we did not create them. What is merely subjective seems to be more or less my own creation. Making use of the psychologists' own language I should like to point out the psychological meaning of this "merely". It may be true that the visible image of a god is some kind of projection; an objectivation by which I put the god before myself, thereby freeing myself somehow of his overwhelming power. Probably for this reason the Jews were forbidden to make any likeness of God. But by describing the god as merely subjective I do precisely the same thing. Now I project his power, not outward on the plane of physical visibility, but inward on the plane of psychological fact. If this power called a god is just psychology, I am prepared to handle it. We have got doctors, after all. Well, wait and see!

The psychological interpretation is probably the best existing way of expressing the reality of the gods in the language of a scientific age. If I was right in the first lecture this expression cannot but be ambiguous. Speaking in philosophical terms I should probably say that the very distinction of objective and subjective reality, of matter and mind, of fact and idea makes it impossible to use any but ambiguous language in interpreting mythical thought. As to my views on the philosophical relevance of these distinctions I must refer your curiosity to the second series of ten lectures which will treat of the philosophy of science. One thing is certain, however, that the very concepts of mind, of subjectivity, or psychology as we understand them today are not appropriate to an expression of what the myths intend to say. In speaking of the soul instead of the mind, as I did several times when explaining the psychological interpretation, I may not have lessened the confusion; thereby I may just have replaced an expression of modern thought and Cartesian metaphysics by an expression of medieval thought and Aristotelian metaphysics. Myth, however, is pre-metaphysical as well as pre-scientific.

Here I come to my second point. The psychological interpretation dissects the unity of the myth. Its relative truth does not make the physical and the political interpretations less true.

If I leave out the somewhat complicated political implications for the moment, I can certainly state that the myth tells the history of nature as well as the history of the soul. It portrays them in one great drama.

Even within the physical interpretation we already remarked the same unity of aspects which would be different to us: the same epic celebrates the unique event of the making of the world and the recurring event of spring's victory over the waters of the winter. We must understand that to mythical thought the two events are essentially identical. Modern science refers recurring events to universal laws of nature. It would find the link between the origin of the world and the recurring events in the world in a cosmogonical theory explaining that unique event of the beginning by applying the same universal laws to it; we shall consider examples of such theories in later lectures. But mythical thought does not possess the category of the universal. Of course it remarks the recurrence of events and it describes them by words which can be generally used. But it tries to make clear the essence of what we describe by laws of nature by using particular illustrative examples. This inverts even its concept of causality as compared to ours. To us the first event could happen because the universal law held even then. To the myth the event can recur every year because it happened once. Because Marduk has overcome Tiâmat once, spring can now overcome winter every year. The god is not, as we might think, expressing the validity of the law, but the law is expressing the power of the god.

An analogous consideration is to be applied to the unity of the physical with the psychological interpretation. Mythical thought does not separate body and mind. In this it does not differ from our direct understanding of our fellow man. The mother who sees her child weep sees the grief present in the tears; that tears and grief are different is a later statement, a statement of reflection. If you listen to me and if you understand what I say you hear the thoughts present in my words; that words and thoughts are different, is again a statement of later reflection. You can only make such statements after the contact of understanding has been disturbed; reflection arises most easily out of that distrust which does not believe that this tear expresses real grief or that my words really say what I mean. Perhaps, if you try to cling to that pre-reflective state of mind, you will understand how the great powers of the soul can have been seen as the great powers of the cosmos, too.

But I cannot enlarge on this problem. The next lecture will lead us to an anti-mythical myth: Genesis I.

3 *Creation in the Old Testament*

THE second lecture was devoted to cosmogonical myths. I hope you still hear their wild and wonderful poetry ringing in your ears, and still keep in your minds the drama of the slaughter of gods by which in their view the world came about.

Now I beg you to listen to a text which you all know well and which I nevertheless want to read to you in its completeness:

> In the beginning God created the heaven and the earth.
>
> And the earth was without form and void; and darkness was upon the face of the deep. And the Spirit of God moved upon the face of the waters.
>
> And God said, Let there be light: and there was light.
>
> And God saw the light, that it was good: and God divided the light from the darkness.
>
> And God called the light Day, and the darkness he called

Night. And the evening and the morning were the first day.

And God said, Let there be a firmament in the midst of the waters, and let it divide the waters from the waters.

And God made the firmament, and divided the waters which were under the firmament from the waters which were above the firmament: and it was so.

And God called the firmament Heaven. And the evening and the morning were the second day.

And God said, Let the waters under the heaven be gathered together unto one place, and let the dry land appear: and it was so.

And God called the dry land Earth; and the gathering together of the waters called he Seas: and God saw that it was good.

And God said, Let the earth bring forth grass, the herb yielding seed, and the fruit tree yielding fruit after his kind, whose seed is in itself, upon the earth: and it was so.

And the earth brought forth grass, and herb yielding seed after his kind, and the tree yielding fruit, whose seed was in itself, after his kind: and God saw that it was good.

And the evening and the morning were the third day.

And God said, Let there be lights in the firmament of the heaven to divide the day from the night; and let them be for signs, and for seasons, and for days, and years:

And let them be for lights in the firmament of the heaven to give light upon the earth: and it was so.

And God made two great lights; the greater light to rule the day, and the lesser light to rule the night: he made the stars also.

And God set them in the firmament of the heaven to give light upon the earth.

And to rule over the day and over the night, and to divide the light from the darkness: and God saw that it was good.

And the evening and the morning were the fourth day.

And God said, Let the waters bring forth abundantly the moving creature that hath life, and fowl that may fly above the earth in the open firmament of heaven.

And God created great whales, and every living creature that moveth, which the waters brought forth abundantly, after their kind, and every winged fowl after his kind: and God saw that it was good.

And God blessed them, saying, Be fruitful, and multiply, and fill the waters in the seas, and let fowl multiply in the earth.

And the evening and the morning were the fifth day.

And God said, Let the earth bring forth the living creature after his kind, cattle, and creeping thing, and beast of the earth after his kind: and it was so.

And God made the beast of the earth after his kind, and cattle after their kind, and every thing that creepeth upon the earth after his kind: and God saw that it was good.

And God said, Let us make man in our image, after our likeness: and let them have dominion over the fish of the sea, and over the fowl of the air, and over the cattle, and over all the earth, and over every creeping thing that creepeth upon the earth.

So God created man in his own image, in the image of God created he him; male and female created he them.

And God blessed them, and God said unto them, Be fruitful, and multiply, and replenish the earth, and subdue it: and have dominion over the fish of the sea, and over the fowl of the air, and over every living thing that moveth upon the earth.

And God said, Behold, I have given you every herb bearing seed, which is upon the face of all the earth, and every tree, in which is the fruit of a tree yielding seed; to you it shall be for meat.

And to every beast of the earth, and to every fowl of the air, and to every thing that creepeth upon the earth, wherein there is life, I have given every green herb for meat: and it was so.

And God saw every thing that he had made, and, behold, it was very good. And the evening and the morning were the sixth day.

Thus the heavens and the earth were finished, and all the host of them.

And on the seventh day God ended his work which he had made; and he rested on the seventh day from all his work which he had made.

And God blessed the seventh day, and sanctified it: because that in it he had rested from all his work which God created and made.

How does this report compare with the cosmogonical myths?

Here, too, a *mythos*, a tale is told. We are still in the realm of mythology. Science has not yet broken the firmament of the heaven. Still a god acts as human beings act; still he speaks to man in human words.

Yet, how great is the difference! Not an infinite epic, but a limited, well-ordered report. No slaughter of the gods, no dragons of the sea, no building of the world out of the slain body of the enemy. A god who has no adversary builds the world like a house, he tends the earth like a garden. The language is not poetry but prose. It is precise and condensed. We should not be deceived by the sound of solemn antiquity with which we inevitably hear it. This language is in fact solemn, but it is solemn in the way of full and sincere lucidity. The age of reason is in the ascendancy.

The contents show the same features as the style.

The world is now seen as an understandable whole. The plan is laid out for completeness. The six days are precisely not naive mythology; they are a means of classification, precursors of Linnaeus' system. No doubt the writer believed in them literally; who would not believe in his own system? The writer really believed that God had created those categories which we use in describing living and dead things. How characteristic of the interest in classification is the repeated phrase "of his kind", "of their kind".

No doubt the elements of the mythical epic are used in several places. But there the myth suffers precisely what it describes as being the fate of the ancient gods: it is slain and its parts are used as materials in a new edifice. Some details of the Biblical report even seem to indicate a conscious polemic against the Babylonian myth. Thus the chaos of the beginning is still remembered: "the earth was without form and void"; *tehóm*, the deep waters of the same verse, is the same word as Tiâmat. But it is not Chaos which has borne the God; no: "In the beginning God created heaven and earth." God was there first and you cannot ask whence he came. That sun and moon are made on the fourth day, long after the creation of light, is most certainly not due to the naive ideas of one who would not have known that daylight comes from the sun. One should rather think that thereby light in its own essence is distinguished from the many sources of light of which sun and moon are but the greatest ones. Here the implicit polemic against the Babylonian astral religion seems evident. Old Testament scholars have told me that the omission of the names Sun and Moon for the great lights is not accidental. These names are the names of gods, but the two lights are no gods; they are lamps made to light the world and to count the days and the seasons.

In spite of these differences the narrative is a holy tale, perhaps even in a stricter sense than the myths. If it is a work of scholarship, it belongs to theology. Its centre is God, not the world. It explains the order of the world by telling how it was made by God.

Who can have written such a story? Modern scholarship has found out that this first chapter of Genesis is to be ascribed to the so-called Priestly Code. This is the youngest of the three main sources of what later times called the Books of Moses. There are very good reasons for assuming that it was written down during the Babylonian captivity of the Jews, in the 6th century BC. Certainly centuries of slow formation can have preceded this final redaction. But the text as we have it seems to have been written in knowledge of, and in opposition to the Babylonian myth.

Probably the intellectual atmosphere of educated circles in Nebuchadnezzar's repristinated Babylonian empire was far more rational, far more "modern" than the state of mind expressed in that time honoured festival hymn which was then still celebrated by the priests. But the hypothetical influence of the rationality of an ageing culture would, I think, be insufficient to explain that solemn lucidity of Genesis I. I am inclined to think that even the enlightened rationality of a nation grows under the shadow of its gods and passes away with them. Our text does not seem to mirror the restlessness of rational refinement but rather an unbroken peace with those deep powers in the soul which find no adequate expression in abstract concepts but which are reached by the image and the voice of the gods. The Jews have been able to interpret the world in a new, non-Babylonian way, because they believed in another god than the Babylonians. The God of the Jews has become the God of the Christians, and nobody will really understand modern Europe who knows nothing about the God of the Jews.

However these historical influences may have been, to the author of Genesis I the world seems understandable precisely because God has made it. Who is this God?

To the pious Jew for whom this tale is written his God is known from his childhood, just as all nations know their gods under whose protection they live. But Yahve, the God of the Jews, is different from the gods of other nations. If I am to express it in the very words of the Jewish tradition, the Jews knew him as the God of Abraham, the God of Moses, the God of the Prophets. We now have to interpret these three names. Abraham stands for faith, Moses for the law, the Prophets for judgment. All of them stand for God's covenant with his people, they stand for God's promise. What does this mean?

Abraham stands for faith. He has been called by God: "Get thee out of thy country, and from thy kindred, and from thy father's house, unto a land that I will shew thee." That was not easily done in a time when the family and the clan were the only protection to a man. But Abraham listens and does what God tells him, he does it then and there. That is precisely what is called *fides*, faith. God promises him: "And I will make of thee a great nation . . . and in thee shall all families of the earth be blessed." The promise is in the future. I must live my faith without seeing the fulfilment of the promise. In all that has been written by man I know no more terrifying example of what faith demands than the offering of Isaac. But the promise is not broken and Isaac may live. "Abraham believed in the Lord; and he counted it to him for righteousness."

Moses stands for the law. From the days of Abraham we see the Jews separated from the nations. Moses unites them to be a nation themselves by the law that God dictated him. God has created a nation by his covenant. From that time on this nation will not be able to live unless it keeps God's covenant. Thereby God is seen to be a God of separation. He severs his people, who have the law, from the other nations who do not have it. In his people he severs those who keep the covenant from those who violate it. Thus originates the opposition of good and evil, an opposition which cannot exist in the same strictness in polytheism where different deities rightly demand different acts. This opposition is not yet an abstract morality. To be good means to keep the covenant, and that means life. To be evil means to break the covenant, and that means death.

The prophets stand for judgment. To be good means life, to be evil means death. But the appearance of life is different. The prophets open the eyes of those who are willing to see the deeper truth. They do it, as everything relevant that is ever done, in and for a well-defined historical situation. Their teaching accompanies the political breakdown of the nation. They teach their nation to understand this event as God's chastisement. This is not to be understood as their cheap outward causality: God will do you good if you obey his laws. Even if the prophets had to use such language in order to be heard by the many, they really understand that to leave the law of God is the deadly thing in itself, not its outward consequences. To leave God s law means to leave the source of life. Hence precisely the judgment makes clear the meaning of the promise: if you stay in faith you will live with God. I think this promise has been fulfilled. Like every state the Jewish state has finally broken down. Like no other nation the Jewish nation has survived the end of its political framework.

How is Genesis I connected with all this? The Old Testament is the history of God's covenant, written down for his people. How must a nation that understands itself in this manner understand the surrounding world? He who has the God of this covenant cannot have other gods before him. The first commandment is the condition under which Jewish life is alone possible. Thereby the existence of other gods is not at all denied. To a nation living in the time of Moses or of David such an idea would have been impossible. We see with our eyes every day how the gods of the heathen live and act in their nations. Just for this reason Yahve is a jealous god. But as the Jews cannot be separated completely from other nations and particularly since the Exile mixed them with one of the greatest nations they cannot just disregard their gods. Our god is the god of good and evil, of life and death; our god is the only true god. This development is not only historically inevitable, it means a great step forward in religious cognition. The Jew cannot but realize that the other nations do not have the same understanding of life and death and thereby of good and evil which is given him by his covenant with God. The terrifying demand of a faith in one god has taken the Jew out of the relativities as well as of the monstrosities of polytheism; he has learnt now a moral lesson which he might not have been able to learn in any other way.

But if this is so, the Jews must understand everything in the world in the light of the true God. He is the god of a historical covenant. Therefore everything in the world must in fact belong to the history of this covenant. Thus the Jews have been the first people to understand the world as history. The book of Genesis weaves every memorable tradition of ancient times into this theology of history. Before the covenant with Abraham it places the covenants with Noah and with Adam, both of which include not just the Jews but all mankind. And before all these covenants it places finally that description of cosmogony which is compatible with the idea of the one true God. The history of creation tells how the stage was set for the history of God's covenant with man.

Hence its concise form, hence its contents. Yahve may well have originally been a thundering wind-god of the desert; now even the rôle of the Lord of Heaven in a Pantheon, the rôle of a Marduk, Zeus, or Odin is too low for him. He cannot have grown out of the world, else there would have been other gods before him. No doubt historians of religion may place him at the side of the deities of light; yet he is not the light, but light was his first work. The history of creation which I read to you is followed, from Genesis 2. 4 on, by an older one, which scholars ascribe to the so-called Yahvist source; there God still forms man like an artisan out of the dust of the ground. In our younger text God creates in the same way in which alone he acts in Jewish life: by his word. "And God said, Let there be . . . And there was . . ."

Since God now is so highly exalted above the whole world, everything in the world is of the same nature: it is a creature of God, it is not God. Thus God himself has deprived the world of its divinity. De-mythologizing has become a common word in our century. If mythology means that our thought is under the domination of the gods, it is precisely the faith in God which has de-mythologized our thinking from the time when the Old Testament was written. That is why I called this history of creation an anti-mythical myth. We will have to watch this process through Christianity till our time.

Everything in the world is God's creature. But one creature is distinguished above all others: man. He is made in the image of God.

I should not doubt, looking at the question historically, that man-shaped idols have made this idea possible. But then, how did man-shaped idols come about and what did they express? A fetish is divine, being the thing it is; it does not need a human face. Animal powers of the soul may incorporate themselves in animal-shaped deities. But man, learning to understand himself as a responsible person, has seen a man-like person in the god who made him such. The God of the Old Testament speaks to me. He says "thou" to me and hence I can say "thou" to him. The personal God is the God who made man to be a person. "I have called thee by thy name, thou art mine."[1] The Jewish religion has finally reduced all our relations with God to this speaking and hearing. Even his likeness could no longer be made by hands. The man-like image of God was hidden or forbidden; he who sees God must die.

Thus we, mankind, who can say "I" and "you" and "we", are made in the image of God just in this personal quality. Hence it is meaningful that God should tell man to subdue the earth. Expressing the same thought less mythologically we may say: if we have faith in God we are no longer the slaves of the gods. The gods are the powers of the world, within and without ourselves. If we have faith in God we are free in the world. This is why Jews and Christians have martyrs, witnesses of this freedom. The same freedom from the gods enables man to a re-shaping dominion of nature. In this sense I think even modern secularization, even scientism cannot be understood without the background of which I am speaking now. I shall come back to this point in later lectures.

But now we approach a dangerous possible misunderstanding.

[1] Isaiah 43. 1.

We have now so clearly distinguished the God of the Jews and the Christians from all pagan gods that we may have come close to the concept called the God of the philosophers by Pascal. The God of the philosophers is a pure spirit, the highest entity, the first cause of the world, all-knowing, almighty, all-bountiful. Wherever in later times we read about God in Jewish, Christian or Mohammedan philosophy and even theology, we find a concept of God that can somehow be described by the attributes just mentioned. It is very important to see that this is not the God of the Old Testament.

Let us begin by one particular attribute, God's spirituality. It is true that the Old Testament speaks of the Spirit of God. But then it does not mean an immaterial principle as opposed to matter. The very concept of matter is foreign in the Bible. Spirit in the Old Testament is breath. Some modern interpreters who know that have even been tempted to translate the *ruach Elohim* of the second verse of our text not by "the Spirit of God" but by "a storm of God". But the sounding voice, the word itself is breath, too. Every animal lives only as long as it breathes. Thus my breath is my life, it is myself as a person, appearing to the senses. Hence the Spirit of God is the Divine Life by which men or women at times can speak God's word and do God's deeds.

Later theologians who were usually spiritualists have read their spiritualism into the Old Testament, thinking that the Bible, being the truth, could only contain what seemed to be truth to them. Even if we take a more critical view we may feel tempted to think that by eliminating all that is mythical from the Old Testament's understanding of God we would arrive at the Most Perfect Being of metaphysical theology. This is not so. In pursuing such an argument we do not arrive at a consistent concept of God but at a paradox.

We can illustrate this by returning once more to the history of the creation in Genesis I. It is one of the most rationally consistent parts of the Bible. I have tried to explain the line of argument that seems to have led to its rather late addition to the body of Biblical tales. Just this consistency has made it a possible starting point of the metaphysical theology of which we will speak in later lectures. But the very same consistency makes it no more than an outpost position of the Bible. I said it was the setting of the stage for the covenant. But the setting is not complete before the serpent has appeared. In fact the tale of the fall is older and theologically more important than the history of creation. For where would we find ourselves if we had only the history of creation? It seems to teach the making of all existing things by an almighty, good God. Later theologians were able to interpret it as teaching the creation of the world out of nothing (*creatio ex nihilo*). All that God made was very good. What else could thence be expected but a history which would be the sheer fulfilment of God's will? But not even philosophers have dared to interpret the real world in such terms; and most definitely this is not the view of the Bible.

To the Bible God is the God who divides good from evil. The good is his work. The evil is not his work; it is rejected by him. Yet the evil is real. Man goes on doing the evil. This is the true picture of the world. Therefore the myth of creation had to be followed by the myth of man's fall. The great poet who wrote this myth in Genesis 3 showed a deep understanding by not saying whence the serpent's subtlety originated. He said precisely as much as he could say and kept silent about the unknowable. In any case only with Adam's and Eve's fall could the real history of the world begin, that history which is a struggle between God and man from the outset. Man has deserted God and deserts him daily. The dialogue between God and man which is the moving force of history has no other theme but to redeem man from his desertion. The covenant is an action in this battle, the desertion from God is death, and God calls me to life whenever he speaks to me. Faith means nothing but the trust in this call.

In the last sentences I have tried to express the true meaning of the Bible on this point. Perhaps this meaning has up to this day never been expressed without the use of some myth; we do not know whether it will ever be possible to express it otherwise. But one thing is certain: whoever for the sake of consistency or of harmony removes this battle from the centre of the picture, will exclude precisely that experience of God from his thought, on which Judaism and Christianity rest.

4 *Greek Philosophy and Cosmogony*

THE Greeks left the house of the myth as well as the Jews, but they left it by a different door and found themselves on a different road thereafter. In their thought the question whence the world has come was transformed into the question what the world is. To them the highest wisdom was not to hear the voice of the living God but to see the immovable essence of being.

Thales taught that the beginning of all things was water. So we are informed by Aristotle. Do these words teach a cosmogony?

Thales of Miletus is the first name we hear in the history of Greek philosophy as well as of Greek mathematics. He lived in the first half of the 6th century BC. Thus he may have been a hundred years younger than Hesiod and perhaps a contemporary of those Jewish priests who wrote the first chapter of Genesis. Very little is known about his person. I feel tempted to think of him as what the 19th century AD would have called a merchant-banker, being a citizen of one of the greatest commercial cities of his time. He would not, perhaps, be the founder of the firm but rather belong to a younger generation; thus he may have had wealth and leisure to see the world and to satiate his immense curiosity, a quality he shared with all of his nation. He was thoughtful. Once, a late anecdote tells us, when contemplating the sky he fell into a cistern, and some women laughed at the man who looked at the heavens and forgot to see what was before him. But according to another story he restored his reputation as a realist. Just as he proved to be able to predict an eclipse of the sun he even seems to have been able to predict the weather; thus by buying up all the oil mills before a season he foresaw as being a good one for the oil crop he did very good business.

The Greek noun which I have translated by "beginning" is *arche*. It belongs to the verb *archein*, which means to be the first one in every respect, whether it be as a beginner or as a ruler. It would be surprising if Thales, in using this word, did not think of a beginning in time.

In putting water at the beginning of all things, Thales does not seem to have expressed a view very different from that of the oriental myths which he no doubt knew. Apsû and Tiâmat are the water. And would Thales, who lived in Asia Minor, not have known the views of one of the greatest civilized nations of his time? He is also said to have thought that the earth as a whole was swimming on water like wood and that in earthquakes it was rocking like a ship. This seems quite a natural idea for a son of a seafaring nation, and it is not yet far away from the myth of the earth-embracing stream Okeanos.

Yet there is another nuance in his view, and probably this nuance means that the time of *mythos* has come to an end and the time of *logos* has begun. Thales calls his beginning water. This is not the name of a god and not the name of the great Divine Things like Earth, Heaven or even Sea. Water is not an individual that exists once; it exists everywhere and more recent thinkers would say that it is a universal concept, not a single thing. The mythical causality begins to be reversed: by putting water in the beginning we explain the beginning by likening it to the things of everyday life.

But then even the concept of beginning, of principle, must change its meaning. If Thales really did think that there was a time in which there was nothing but water, how can the other materials and things have originated from water? Shall we not be compelled to say that they really are water? Experience teaches us that water can be changed into ice and into steam, and that steam and ice can be changed back into water. Just for that reason we say today that ice and steam are nothing but water in a different state. And if everything has come from water, water must be what later thinkers would call the substance of the world. This is what Aristotle understood Thales to have meant. Water is then the principle of all things: all things are water. The question whence the world has come has been changed by its own logic into the question what the world is: cosmogony has been transformed into ontology.

But then the answer that all things are water or any other stuff cannot be satisfactory. If everything is water, what do we mean by "water"? How are we to distinguish that water which appears as water from the other water which appears as stones, grass and cows? Certainly we should not confound the real thing with one of its appearances. It seems that the beginning of our sentence, "all things are . . ." is a very profound question to which the end ". . . water" gives a very superficial answer. Now the water which first was seen to be the starting-point of a non-mythical analysis of the world appears on a higher level of reflection like a remnant of the mythical world-view. Perhaps we may compare this idea of water to a hook on which the fish of the question about being was caught.

Philosophies that took this question in its full seriousness have not always returned to cosmogony at all. When they did, their cosmogonies were more or less the myths of their respective ontologies; they were ways of explaining their interpretation of being in the easier language of narration. Hence from here on cosmogony cannot be separated from ontology. We shall follow the path of Greek ontology in a few rapid steps which unfortunately cannot but be somewhat superficial.

Things are perhaps water. Rather not water. But they are

something. What are they? What do we mean by "being something"?

In any case they are. They exist. What is "to exist"? What is being?

It is the historic accomplishment of Parmenides from Elea to have first asked these questions clearly and abstractly. He expressed them, as usually happens, not as questions but as answers, not as doubts but as affirmations. His affirmations are so abstract that up to this day there is no agreement about their meaning. But just because their meaning remained debatable they influenced all later thought like questions. A later philosopher who wanted to assert or deny Parmenides' position had first to restate it; he had to give his own interpretation of what being meant.

I shall not try to be wiser than ancient philosophers or modern philologists; I shall not try to explain what Parmenides meant to say. But I must quote as much of him as will be needed to understand his influence on later Greek thought:

> Come now, and I will tell thee
> and do thou hearken and carry my word away
> the only ways of enquiry that can be thought of:
> the one way, that it is and cannot not-be,
> is the path of Persuasion, for it attends upon Truth;
> the other, that it is-not and needs must not-be,
> that I tell thee is a path altogether unthinkable.
> For thou couldst not know that which is-not nor utter it;
> for the same thing can be thought as can be.[1]

This is certainly a good and modern translation. Every translation, in a text of this degree of abstraction, is an interpretation. I prefer to express the fourth line of this text in a clumsy literal translation which tries not to make the English text more easily understood than is the Greek text. It would then read, that the first way of investigation says: "The one, that is, and that not-being is not." It says "that is". The "is" has no grammatical subject. Some interpreters have thought the text to be corrupt;

[1] Translation by G. S. Kirk and J. E. Raven in *Presocratic Philosophers*, C.U.P.

or at least, that a particular subject should be inserted. But which subject should we insert? That something is? That an existing thing is? That nothing but existing things are? That one thing only is? That being is? I am inclined to think that the text is not corrupt, and that Parmenides would have been able to say all that if he had wanted to say it. He goes on to say: and that not-being is not. Wrong is the way that not-being is, and wrong is the way that both being and not-being are.

But then being can have no beginning.

> One way only is left to be spoken of, that it is;
> and on this way are full many signs that what is
> is uncreated and imperishable,
> for it is entire, immovable and without end.
> It was not in the past, nor shall it be,
> since it is now, all at once, one, continuous;
> for what creation wilt thou seek for it?
> how and whence did it grow?
> Nor shall I allow thee to say or to think,
> 'from that which is not';
> for it is not to be said or thought that it is not.
> And what need would have driven it on to grow,
> starting from nothing, at a later time rather than
> an earlier?
> Thus it must either completely be or be not.
> Nor will the force of true belief allow that,
> beside what is, there could also arise anything
> from what is not;
> wherefore Justice looseth not her fetters to allow it
> to come into being or perish, but holdeth it fast;
> and the decision on these matters rests here:
> it is or it is not.
> But it has surely been decided, as it must be,
> to leave alone the one way as unthinkable and nameless
> (for it is no true way),
> and that the other is real and true.

How could what is thereafter perish?
and how could it come into being?
For if it came into being, it is not,
nor if it is going to be in the future.
So coming into being is extinguished and perishing
unimaginable.[1]

Being thus is opposed to any temporality. According to Parmenides being "was not" and "will not be", for this would imply change. Being is and changes not. Speaking of Thales we said that if things grew out of water they somehow still are water, so that water is the unchanging principle of being. This same thought seems here to be formulated on its adequate level of abstraction, leaving out the unphilosophical specification of being as water.

But whenever a thought is made rigid and consistent, its inherent paradoxes begin to stand out clearly. If being cannot change, change cannot be. But our world is a world of change. Is it therefore not being? What would this mean? We started asking how the world came to be. We went on asking what the world is. We then asked what being is. We found that being is unchangeable and coming to be unthinkable. Thus we found the idea of being and we lost its applicability to this world of change.

Parmenides himself, however, devoted the second half of his poem to cosmogony. The greater part of this second half is lost. But we know that he considered it not to present truth as the first half did, but *doxa*, i.e. opinion. Is opinion in his view false opinion? If it is, why does he propose it? If it is not, what does he mean by the distinction of opinion and truth?

Here the later philosophers take their starting point. They accept the timeless, unchanging nature of being. Then they have to explain the changing aspects of the world. They have to say either how change can be, or else in what sense the changing world we know may be not-being. They have to explain that by first saying what they understand by being. I shall describe

[1] Kirk and Raven, *op. cit.*

just two different solutions of this problem: the theory of atoms of Leucippus and Democritus, and the theory of forms of Plato.

Everything that is, consists of indivisible parts, the atoms. All differences between things are differences of the shapes, positions, and motions of their atoms. All change is a change of the positions of atoms. Besides the atoms, nothing exists.

Never has a simpler explanation of the world been offered than this. It is not necessary to advertise it in our time, when the atom has taken over even the headlines of the newspapers. It may be more important to point out in what sense modern atomic physics does not agree with this simple picture of ancient atomism. But that is to be left to the second series of lectures. It is now my task to say more clearly what kind of a philosophy ancient atomism really was.

Leucippus, its founder, is said to have been a disciple of Parmenides. Democritus, who was the most famous disciple of Leucippus, lived to be an elder contemporary of Plato. Epicurus, the Hellenistic philosopher of wise contentment—who by one of the strange misinterpretations of which history is full has given his name to an unrestrained indulgence in sensual pleasures—carried the doctrine further, and our main literary source about it, Lucretius Carus in his poem *De Rerum Natura*, considers him to be its real founder.

In order to remind ourselves of the immense power of explanation of this doctrine it is sufficient to think of the transformation of water into ice or steam. This is now to be understood as changes of the order and the state of motion of the atoms. In ice the atoms have fixed places like students in their rows of seats. When the ice melts into water they begin to move past each other, but still in close contact, comparable to the students who are just leaving the lecture hall. In steam they fly freely through space just as the students will take their individual ways home alone or in little groups, the molecules. In this precise setting the explanation of the "states of aggregation" is, in fact, modern, but I think it corresponds very well to the intention of ancient atomism.

But we would not understand ancient atomism rightly if we took it to be mainly a scientific hypothesis, trying to explain observed phenomena. It is even a fact that the main development of those sciences in which antiquity excelled most, mathematics and astronomy, was closely connected with the philosophical school that was strictly opposed to the atomists, the school of Plato; I shall point to the probable reasons for this fact later. Atomism was a philosophy. It was an attempt to solve the speculative problem of being. From the point of view of modern science this may seem to be a weakness, an overloading of the boat that had to cross the ocean of experience with a ballast of metaphysical stones. I agree that its dogmatic character was a weakness. But that is the weakness of most historical philosophy. Philosophers tend to become famous not for their good questions but for their premature answers. And if I have described scientism rightly, it is a sort of unconscious philosophy itself, not less dogmatic for not being conscious of its dogmatism. In any case, quantum theory, as I hope to show in the second series of lectures, has forced back upon us physicists precisely some of those philosophical questions which the empirical atomism of the nineteenth century had thought fit to avoid.

What, then, is the solution of the Eleatic problem of being, as offered by ancient atomism?

To Parmenides being is one and unchanging; not-being is not; change is not being. The atomists start by defining more closely what they mean by being. The only existing things are the atoms. Being is one. Hence an atom is one. It has no parts. Thence it follows that it cannot be divided. While to modern thought the phrase that the atom is one would be a somewhat obscure expression of its practical indivisibility, to ancient atomism its absolute indivisibility is a natural consequence of its ontological quality of being one. You may as well argue from the unchanging nature of being. Division would be a change. Hence atoms, if they deserve the predicate of being at all, must be indivisible. The statement that atoms are indivisible is an ontological proposition.

This theory seems to offer a wonderful solution to the problem of the reality of change. Water can change, it can be transformed into ice or steam. But water does not exist in the strict sense, it is an aspect of the atoms. The atoms of water cannot change, they are truly existing. But their positions and states of motion change. Thus you can choose whether you like to call change real: it really takes place but it does not change the really existing things.

But we are allowed to doubt whether this clever trick really makes the paradox of change and being disappear. In identifying the atoms with being, the atomists have tacitly sacrificed two central ideas of the Eleatic philosophy: the uniqueness of being and the non-existence of not-being. To say "the atom is one and hence indivisible" is all right; but there are many atoms, and they are needed to explain the world. The atomists did not even consider the atoms to be equal. There are big atoms and small atoms, rough square atoms of earth, finer atoms of fire, and the very fine, round and smooth all-pervading atoms of the soul. We may avoid this objection by interpreting "being" not as a subject but as a predicate, the common predicate of all existing things, even if we have to admit that this way of expression presupposes a logic, not yet developed in Democritus' time. But even then we do not avoid the second, or graver contradiction. Democritus says quite clearly himself that atomism has to admit the existence of non-being: *to meden* exists as well as *to den*, a pun in Greek which might be rendered in English by saying: "Nothing exists as well as 'thing'." He is speaking of the void.

In fact, if atoms lay packed contiguously without any intervals, no motion would be possible. The space into which an atom is to move must be free for it. Atomism has always assumed the existence of empty space. Now we must not forget that the concept of absolute space as we know it from Newton is modern. Equally modern is the idea that geometry is a science whose subject matter is space. Greek geometry was about points, finite straight lines, triangles, circles, cubes, spheres and so on; it did not even have a word for space. Similarly the atomists had no word like our "space"; they spoke of *to kenon*, the void. But to speak of the void as existing is a paradox, if we take the Eleatic starting point of the atomists seriously. The void is empty of existing things, it is a kind of not-being. If it were being, it would have to be built from atoms itself, because we started by saying that the atoms were the only being. Thus again the rigid consequence of thought has produced a paradox. By apparently conserving the Eleatic theory of being in one point, in the atoms, this philosophy is forced to contradict the same theory of being in the other point, the void. Once it has thus incorporated the paradox in its very foundations, it can draw all its further conclusions with apparently perfect rationality. It is a pity that we do not know Democritus' answer to this problem since all his books are lost except for a few fragments. In the popularizing poet Lucretius we cannot expect an understanding of the rigour of thought that prevailed in the great times of Greek philosophy; he says nothing about the question.

Can atomism give us a cosmogony?

Since atoms cannot change they cannot have originated. Thus cosmogony cannot mean the coming to be of atoms. They have always existed and they will exist for ever. But cosmos means order. Order can have arisen out of disorder in the world of ever-existing atoms. In this sense there is an atomistic cosmogony. In Kathleen Freeman's book on the pre-Socratic philosophers[1] it is briefly and fairly described in the following terms:

> Many atoms of differing shapes separate off from the infinite mass and come together in a great empty space. Here, having collected, they form an eddy, that is, they begin to move round in a circle. As they jostle together in this revolution,

[1] *Companion to the Pre-Socratic Philosophers*, Blackwell.

like goes to like: the light atoms fly outwards, the rest stay together. Of the latter, certain hook-shaped atoms, being interlocked, form a kind of outer skin, globe-shaped, enclosing the rest; this is the sky. In the centre are the bodies borne there, and now cleaving together, except for some which fly outward and are retained by the outer skin, which keeps whatever touches it; these are the heavenly bodies. All is now revolving round the central mass, which is the material from which earth is made. The motion caused the drying up of this mass, and the squeezing out of the water, so that earth and sea were separated.

First I want to say a few words about the astronomical merits of this picture. You see that the earth is now considered to be a sphere in the centre of the world, and that the sky is another sphere, surrounding the earth. This is a great step forward compared with the earlier view which thought of the earth like a flat disk and of the sky like a hemisphere. The Greeks had recognized the spherical shape of the earth at an early time by correctly interpreting the way in which a ship disappears behind the horizon and the circular shape of the earth's shadow at lunar eclipses. A second progress is the idea that it is not the stars which wander over the sky but that the sky as a whole is a sphere which rotates around the earth, carrying the stars with it. This view is no longer held today. But I think that just by being on a higher level of abstraction than the idea that sun and stars wander individually, it is a progress in the right direction; once the sky is understood to move as a whole in relation to the earth it will be an easier step to reverse the order of motions by saying that the sky stands still and the earth rotates. In fact, this view was held by later Greek astronomers like Aristarchus; the reason why Greek astronomy finally rejected it I shall consider in the sixth lecture.

What I have just said about the spheres of earth and heaven was common Greek knowledge at the time of the atomist philosophers. Probably their own contribution lies in the idea that this rotating heavenly sphere had originated in a huge eddy of atoms. This proved to be a very useful idea; you will see its application in modern theories like those of Descartes, of Kant and of 20th century astronomers. Nor did the atomists confine their consideration to this world, that is to this one earth on which we live with its own sky. They thought that the universe was infinite, containing an infinite number of atoms which form an infinite number of worlds which originate in the way I described and are destroyed in due course by new mixtures of the atoms. This idea, too, has been taken up by the modern theories mentioned above. Thus, in a way, scientists of our time may feel quite at home in the world of Leucippus and Democritus.

Yet there is another side of the coin. Modern science rests on a quantitative description of phenomena; it rests on the concept of mathematical laws of nature. I have not been able to find the slightest indication of this idea in Greek atomism. A critical modern scientist might find the sketch of atomistic cosmogony which I read to you very similar to some rather bad popular modern representations of the world-view of science. There is an impressive imagery of eddies, of different-shaped atoms sticking together, like going to like, light atoms moving outward, heavy ones inward without a clear concept of gravitation or of buoyancy: a story plausible to the unscientific mind, neither explaining what follows mathematically nor formulating a guarded hypothesis, but telling what might have happened as though it were plain truth; it is a tale of becoming, a myth.

I should like to call the atomistic cosmogony a myth of science. The god in whom these myth-tellers believe is the blind necessity of atomic collisions. This anti-religious element of atomism was consistent. If there are man-shaped gods at all they cannot be anything but bodies formed from atoms since atoms are the only existing things; thus before there might have been a god who planned a creation there must have been a blind agglomeration of atoms out of which the god originated by pure chance. This is, of course, only a late consequence of a view which denies the gods of the myth from the outset. Whenever I dare to say precisely what is the nature of every existing thing the god who is greater than all my thoughts has disappeared; this complete objectivation of the world is identical with a negation of the numinous. And this is what atomism intends. Epicurus is courteous enough to admit the existence of gods who live a life of inactive bliss in the intermundia, the empty spaces between the "worlds"; they do not concern themselves with human life. Lucretius writes his poem for a friend in order to free him from the fear of gods and of punishments in another world, those inventions of priests longing for power. After having described how Iphigenia was sacrificed to priestly prejudice he writes the famous line: *Tantum religio potuit suadere malorum*, so powerful was religion to mislead mankind towards evil. When in the later centuries of antiquity even the intellectuals longed for a revival of religion, this anti-religious tendency proved fateful for the atomistic school of philosophy. It had to wait for the 17th century to be resumed.

Let us now come to the other solution of the Eleatic problem: Plato's philosophy. I read to you a part of Plato's cosmogonical dialogue, the *Timaeus*, in Cornford's translation.

> We must then, in my judgment, first make this distinction: What is that which is always real and has no becoming and what is that which is always becoming and never real? That which is apprehensible by thought with a rational account is the thing that is always unchangeably real; whereas that which is the object of belief together with unreasoning sensation is the thing that becomes and passes away, but never has real being. Again, all that becomes must needs become by the agency of some cause; for without a cause nothing can come to be. Now whenever the maker of anything looks to that which is always unchanging and uses a model of that description in fashioning the form and quality of his work, all that he thus accomplishes must be

good. If he looks to something that has come to be and uses a generated model, it will not be good.

So concerning the whole Heaven or World—let us call it by whatsoever name may be most acceptable to it—we must ask the question which, it is agreed, must be asked at the outset of inquiry concerning anything: Has it always been, without any source of becoming; or has it come to be, starting from some beginning? It has come to be; for it can be seen and touched and it has body, and all such things are sensible; and, as we saw, sensible things, that are to be apprehended by belief together with sensation, are things that become and can be generated. But again, that which becomes, we say, must necessarily become by the agency of some cause. The maker and father of this universe it is a hard task to find, and having found him it would be impossible to declare him to all mankind. Be that as it may, we must go back to this question about the world: After which of the two models did its builder frame it—after that which is always in the same unchanging state, or after that which has come to be? Now if this world is good and its maker is good, clearly he looked to the eternal; on the contrary supposition (which cannot be spoken without blasphemy), to that which has come to be. Everyone, then, must see, that he looked to the eternal; for the world is the best of things that have become, and he is the best of causes. Having come to be, then, in this way, the world has been fashioned on the model of that which is comprehensible by rational discourse and understanding and is always in the same state.[1]

This is the beginning of a long description of the creation of the world, and it is a very condensed summary of Plato's philosophy. Three elements are to be distinguished in it: First the world that somehow has come to be. Secondly he who made it, whom

[1] *Plato's Cosmology: The Timaeus*, translated by F. M. Cornford, 27d-29a, Routledge.

Plato at times calls the God, at times the craftsman (*demiourgos*), and in a few poetic parts the father of the universe. Thirdly that invariable being that served as a model according to which the world was made.

Here again we have the changing things which are not strictly being and the being that changes not. But their relationship is again a different one: the immovable being is the archetype, the changing things are its copies. What did Plato mean by archetype and copies?

Since it is science we want to understand, let me use a scientific example. Take a pencil and a sheet of paper and draw a circle. Please do it yourself; it is an experience not to be replaced by just thinking of it. You will not produce a good circle. A second or third one may be better but not satisfactory. With a compass you will do better. But look at it with a magnifying glass or even use a microscope. You will see hills of graphite, roughly round like the mountain-ranges on the moon. Finally you will have learnt your lesson: we are unable to produce a perfect material circle. There is no real circle in this world.

But we have wonderful mathematical propositions about circles, e.g. that the circle of all closed figures of equal circumference is that which has the largest area. These propositions are true, they can be proved. But what are they about if there are no circles in the world? Material so-called circles just look like true circles. Mathematical propositions are about what sense-objects look like. The way a thing looks would in Greek be called its *eidos* or its idea. Mathematical propositions are about the *eidos*, the idea, they are about the archetype of which sense-objects are unsatisfactory copies. They are not about this or that thing we may call a circle, they are about the circle itself. You can also say: physical circles are supposed to be shaped according to the mathematical circle. Mathematical propositions are not about material things but about shapes. The material thing "is" not a shape, it "has" or "takes on" a shape. It thus has or takes its part (it participates, *metechei* in Plato's Greek) in those structural qualities which strictly speaking only belong to the shape in its rigorous mathematical sense. Shape is called *morphe* in Greek, *forma* in Latin. Mathematical propositions are about forms. Form is the word by which many modern English texts translate Plato's idea now, in order to avoid confusion with the completely different meaning of the English word idea. English idea means something in the mind, something merely subjective; Plato's idea means the highest degree of objectivity. For the idea is the only thing about which there is strict science. How this change of meaning has come about I shall explain in the next lecture.

But are forms real? Mathematics is a science about things thought of. To the modern mind this implies that it is not about real things, since we are accustomed to call sense-objects real. If you want to understand Plato you will have to eradicate this view from your minds. You will be permitted to re-introduce it in following the further course of history. But now follow this argument: Mathematical propositions are precise and their truth does not depend on time. Statements about sense-objects are ever unprecise, and what was true yesterday may be false today. Yesterday my car's wheel was something like a circle; this morning I had an accident and now the wheel is egg-shaped. But, as Parmenides said, being is without change, and truth is about being; about changing things there is but changing opinion. Hence mathematics, just because it relies on thought and not on sense-perception, is about existing things, while physics is about their unreliable copies in the world of the senses.

This, I think, explains why mathematics flourished in the Platonic school but not in the school of the atomists. Both schools agree that true understanding is possible only about real being. Now, if atoms are the only real being, how can statements about such imaginary things as mathematical spheres, triangles and so on be true knowledge? Precisely if the atomists took their philosophy in a strict sense they could not develop strict mathematics; then there cannot be a science about "the circle" but only about circular arrangements of atoms. Thus, I think, atomism lacked the most important ingredient of the idea of mathematical laws of nature: the belief in the relevance of mathematics. Platonism, on the other hand, lacked the less important part: the belief that mathematics can be strictly applied to nature. Thus atomism produced no mathematical physics at all, while Plato in his *Timaeus* says that one cannot give a strict science of nature but that we must here be satisfied by "telling a likely story". The Greeks are the only nation which came close to a mathematical theory of nature before modern times; they even gave some beautiful examples of such a theory, e.g. in astronomy. Still they did not achieve it in its full breadth. One of the hindrances may well have been that their philosophical theories did not lead them to consider a full mathematical description of nature as possible. If this were true, just the rigour of their philosophical thought in their most productive period may have proved detrimental to their natural science, while it so intensely promoted the development of their equally rigorous mathematics.

Now, speaking of mathematics, I did not choose Plato's own starting-point. His first concern was not about geometry but about man. Following Socrates he did not ask about the circle itself, but about bravery itself, about beauty itself, about virtue itself, of which the single instances of bravery, of beauty, of virtue are nothing but incomplete examples or copies. Love, Eros, kindled by the sight of a beautiful body reminds the soul of beauty itself. The myth of reincarnation tells us that the soul has seen beauty itself in an earlier, now forgotten life. He who remains longing for the beloved beautiful body will not understand his own love better than the mathematician, if he confounds the circle on paper with the true circle, has understood his mathematics. Both content themselves with a mocking reflection of the true light. He who understands the truth of his own love will love the soul of the beloved one. For the soul is the place in which the truth appears, and true love is only possible to souls who find each other in the love of truth. The same structure prevails in the political field. The true order of the state can only be found if we follow the example of original truth. Political passion which understands itself rightly is the longing for the realization of the unchanging order of truth in the changing medium of human life. Therefore the true statesman must be a philosopher.

Even from the point of view of clear understanding, mathematics does not deserve the highest rank in Plato's thought. The mathematician, it is true, draws strict conclusions from given premises, but the premises themselves he just assumes without being able to prove them. I shall remind you of this deep insight into the nature of mathematics when, in the second series of lectures, I shall speak about mathematics from a modern point of view. In the view of Plato, true cognition ought to give an account even of the presuppositions of mathematics. This account is one of the tasks of his theory of forms. What do we mean by saying that only the "circle itself" has true being, while "circles" of the sensual world, coming-to-be and passing away, have their imperfect being only by their "participation" in the being of the "circle itself"? The simple sentence "this pencil-drawn curve has the shape of a circle" contains the whole problem. What do we mean by "it has a shape" ("partakes in it" as Plato says)? What "is" a shape? Plato uses the terms archetype and image. Yet evidently this is itself a simile. If true cognition refers to the form only, then the participation of changing things in the form can essentially be expressed only by the same imprecise imagery by which we must be satisfied in speaking of the world of change itself.

What, then, is a form? This very question is the question about the highest element of Plato's thought, the *idea tou agathou*, the Form of the Good. The good of which he speaks here is not primarily the morally good; on the contrary, Plato's ethics can only be understood by an interpretation of what he means by the good. Schematically we may describe the Form of the

Good as the Form of Forms, the Essence of Essence. If you draw a circle well, it is a "good circle". Yet it will not be really good; the only really good circle is the true circle, the circle itself, the form of the circle. The good circle is that in which all the different empirical circles participate as far as they are (relatively) good. In philosophy we are interested in different forms, you can say in different goods: that of the circle, of bravery, of beauty and so on. They have something in common: they are all forms, they are all good. What is the form in which they thereby participate? It must be called the form of forms, the Form of the Good. In the Simile of the Cave the changing things are likened to shadows. He who leaves the cave sees the things themselves—that is the forms—in the light of the sun. The sun in whose light they are seen is the *idea tou agathou*.

In investigations like this the very meaning of all the available words is in question at every step. Hence Plato must make use of similes on every level. Thus we ought not to consider the relationship of the form of the good to the realm of forms to be a schematic repetition of the relationship of the single forms to the world of the senses. And we can be assured that Plato did not ascribe to his forms a thing like existence, some hypostasized "being in itself" in a "heaven of ideas". Plato was most certainly not what modern logicians call a Platonist. If he defines the form as that which is, then only the form of the forms, the *idea tou agathou* itself represents what we would schematically call the quality of being, and he explicitly says that it is not existent in the sense in which the other forms exist; it is "beyond existence". Hence it would be contrary to his explicitly stated view to explain the being of forms by comparing it to the existence of sensual things. We cannot here follow these central problems of Plato's philosophy, but we ought to see how they are mirrored in the *Timaeus*.

Besides the changing copies and the unchanging archetype our text from *Timaeus* contained a third element, the god who has formed this world as a copy of the archetype. This is not one of the known gods of Greek religion. It seems that no Greek thinker or poet before Plato had ever uttered the idea of a creator of the world. No wonder that the Christians of later times understood Plato to be the pagan sage who came closest to the revealed truth. On the other hand interpreters who have tried to understand Plato strictly in philosophical terms, from the ancient Academy to the modern philologists, have commonly thought of this divine craftsman as a mythical circumscription of an abstract thought. As far as Plato's conscious intention goes I am inclined to share this second view. It is well known how often Plato resorts to a *mythos*, a tale, where he does not consider an abstract exposition possible or understandable to the reader. Plato's myths are never naive; they are works of art which admit of strict interpretation. I think the only strict interpretation possible for the *demiourgos* is that he is such a work of art pointing to something else. This need not inhibit Christians, however, from thinking that something more than his conscious philosophical intention may have guided Plato's artistic inspiration when he wrote the *Timaeus*.

The interpretation which I follow here thinks that Plato chose the myth of creation in order to describe as a sequence in time what he really considered to be the timeless structure of the world. This is similar to the way in which a complicated geometrical structure is explained by drawing it on paper step by step before the eyes of the pupil. Similarly a fictitious process of foundation serves Plato in his *Republic* to analyse the structure of a model community. In this sense I should like to call the *Timaeus* a scientific myth, a story told by a scientific mind and somehow in terms of science. What Plato certainly meant was that the world was "always becoming", which seems to indicate that everything in the world has a beginning and an end. But it does not follow that the world itself had a beginning; and Plato explicitly denies that it will have an end. Aristotle who never resorted to myths certainly held the world to be without a beginning and an end, thus transferring an aspect of Parmenidean being to the world as a whole just as the Atomists had transferred it to the atoms. I see no necessity to assume Plato to have held a corresponding view but it seems more plausible to me than the contrary. In any case Plato does not treat the *demiourgos* as a god to be religiously revered and he never speaks of him in any work besides the *Timaeus*.

If I were speaking of Plato's cosmogony on its own merits I now ought to devote a further lecture to the details of the *Timaeus*, for instance his elaborate mathematical models of what in his view correspond to the atoms. In our actual context, however, I shall only mention one further point: the origin of that which is not good.

It is as natural to Plato as to the Bible to see God as the source of the existence of all that is good. When the Biblical report of the creation was interpreted as representing a creation out of nothing, the insoluble theological problem of the origin of evil was born. Plato does not yet see a problem here.

The maker of the universe is good. To imagine his work to be other than as good as possible is a supposition "which cannot be spoken without blasphemy". Still the world is not perfect; it is only as perfect as possible. For the *demiourgos* is not almighty, and he has not created the world out of nothing—two views which Plato probably never considered even as possibilities. Speaking in speculative strictness the very sense of the concept "good" implies that there is something that is not good; hence interpreting being itself by the form of the good means to admit the presence of something opposed to the good. But what do we now mean by "presence" and "something"? The answer to these questions is given in mythical language in the *Timaeus*.

> The god took over all that is visible—not at rest, but in inconstant and unordered motion—and brought it from disorder into order, since he judged that order was in every way the better.[1]
>
> For the generation of this universe was a mixed result of

[1] *Timaeus*, 30a.

the combination of Necessity and Reason. Reason overruled Necessity by persuading her to guide the greatest part of the things that become towards what is best; in that way and on that principle this universe was fashioned in the beginning by the victory of reasonable persuasion over Necessity.[1]

Thus there are two principles acting in the world: the order of divine reason and the chance of blind necessity. To a modern ear it may sound strange to find necessity identified with chance. Here we must remember the atomists. Plato accepts their interpretation of necessity. Necessity is the inevitable effect of the collision of the spatial elements, the atoms; and those collisions are not guided by any law that would be understandable to reason, they happen blindly. Modern times, giving the concept of necessity a new, precise, sense by means of the concept of mathematical laws of nature, thus interpret necessity itself, quite differently from Plato, by means of that order which Plato calls the form. Here we see why Bentley, still using Plato's concept of blind necessity, was inconsistent after the invention of the concept of all-pervading mathematical laws of nature. To Plato necessity is what we cannot foretell while all that we can foresee is a planned work of reason. Thus to him the perfection of the world is caused by its participation in the divine forms, its imperfection by the action of necessity.

This Platonic description of the universe is the starting point of two later views on the origin of evil that were often used in combination: One of them considered evil to be non-being, the other one derived evil from matter as opposed to the spirit.

The view that evil is non-being can be justified in Platonic terms. A thing is good as far as it participates in its form. Since the form alone has true existence, that in the sensible things which is not good appears as a lack of existence. But can this doctrine be reconciled with the Biblical understanding of Good and Evil? Perhaps it offers a very profound interpretation of the Biblical

[1] *Op. cit.*, 48a.

thought that good means life, evil means death; only that which is good has true existence, that is true life. Yet in the Bible, which does not use philosophical abstractions, evil appears as a reality in face of which a decision is needed. Plato's writings abound in exhortations that we must make the decision for the good; and yet we seem to feel that evil in the Biblical sense is still different from Plato's *kakon*, the absence of the good. And the interpretation of evil as non-being does not remove the paradox of *creatio ex nihilo*; why should God, if he is all-bountiful, have made creatures that are so horribly lacking in being?

If we derive evil from matter, and if we mean by matter what the *demiourgos* "took over", then this is the same doctrine as before. There is no knowledge of formless matter, precisely because it lacks what alone can be known, namely form; it cannot even be said what formless matter is. In the same sense Aristotle calls *prote hyle*, matter apart from all form, unknowable. Yet later dualistic systems considered matter to be a positive power which was opposed to light, to reason, to God. It would be worth while to contemplate these systems in their sombre grandeur. Here this would lead us too far. In any case they are neither Biblical—for the Bible does not originally know the concept of Matter—nor are they Platonic—for the Greeks of classical times did not know the Biblical understanding of evil.

5 *Christianity and History*

CHRISTIANITY is, historically speaking, the religion founded by Jesus who was called the Christ.

I dare not speak about the man Jesus. I do not feel equal to that task. But I owe it to you to make my personal position clear. I am a Christian, or I should rather say: I try to be a Christian. This is not a traditionalist's position. I have even found much of the Christian tradition, both in thought and in life, difficult to understand, and some of it impossible to follow. But, if this is a possible English phrase, I have been hit by the word of Christ. In a way this word has made life impossible to me; the life I might have lived without it has been destroyed by it. In a way it has made life possible to me; I am not certain whether I would have found a possible way of life without it at all. His word means his teaching. But since this teaching refers to life, his word should be understood to include the reports we have about his life, his death, and that mysterious event of which his disciples spoke as his resurrection.

But these lectures are not intended to contain personal confession but critical thought. I had to make my own position clear for what you may call a methodical reason. Let me use science as an example. Science rests on experience. If you discuss a scientific theory it is not necessary that you should have made the relevant experiments yourself. But you must know what scientific experience is, and you ought to make it quite clear to what particular experiments you are referring. Religion equally rests on experience. Experience, in religion as well as in science, is always particular experience. It will be difficult to understand any religion if you do not have the experience of living within a particular religion. In religions like Judaism and Christianity the relevant experience cannot be had without a personal decision. The act of the decision, if it really happens, is itself an integrating part of the experience. Hence, if you want to speak clearly about religion you will have to indicate what decision you have taken.

A decision chooses one way and rejects the other ways. Hence in opening an experience it cuts me off from other experiences. Making a decision cuts me off from some fields of religious truth, for the other religions contain their truth, too; avoiding a decision, however, will cut me off from the whole field of that truth which cannot be had by just looking at it. I do not say that this necessarily means a final cut-off. There is, I believe, an internal structure in the realm of truth, and, having gone through the experience of decision, we may understand in the end even that truth whose experience we rejected. But this process may well last a few thousand years.

The Christian Church originated as the community of those who, as I have tried to express it, were hit by the word of Christ and who tried to live a life according to what they understood to be his will. The language in which they expressed the experience in so living had to be a language they knew. This was to a large extent a language which we would call mythical today. Here is the problem in our interpretation of Christianity. We want to express our experience in a language that comes naturally to us. Are we to abandon myth for the sake of what we take to be rational sincerity and to run the risk of thereby losing the very experience that was expressed in the mythical language? Or are we to retain the mythical language? Can we use it, knowing it is mythical? Are we so sure that we know what is myth and what is not myth? Do we even know sufficiently well what we mean by myth? I have not so far given any rational definition of myth in these lectures.

We shall come back to these questions at the end of this series of lectures. Now I shall try to describe Christianity as it has understood itself, and for this purpose I shall use the concepts introduced in the earlier lectures.

Christianity originated within the Jewish religion. This religion I have tried to describe by the three concepts of faith, of law, and of judgment. These three concepts are retained in Christianity but with a new interpretation. I think it is not wrong to say that faith, law and judgment have been transformed into the Pauline triad of faith, charity, and hope.

Faith is still faith in the God of the Jews whom Jesus taught his disciples to call our father. But it is now at the same time faith in a man, in Jesus himself. This was not less paradoxical then than it is today. It is the paradox which is expressed in the Gospel of St. John by saying: The word was made flesh (1.14). The word (*logos*) in the language here used is the power of God by which the world has been created. Flesh means man, living in this world. If I wanted to interpret the verse precisely I should have to speak of the Gnostic meaning of the two concepts word and flesh; there they are opposites exaggerating Plato's distinction of reason and matter into a strict dualism, and the paradox of the verse becomes even more stringent then. But even without such an interpretation, staying within the Jewish religion, we can see that the verse identifies God's creative power with a creature that has lived once in history. Thus it draws even creation itself into that battle between God and man which is history. The appearance of one man in history who did not fight against God but who really fulfilled his will is understood as a second creation. The meaning of this second creation is seen in the transformation of law into charity, and of judgment into hope.

The Jewish law meant charity. When Jesus says: "Thou shalt love the Lord thy God with all thy heart, and with all thy soul, and with all thy mind . . . and thou shalt love thy neighbour as thyself"[1], he is quoting from the Old Testament.[2] He rightly says: "On these two commandments hang all the law and the

[1] Matt. 22. 37–9. [2] Deut. 6. 5 and 19. 19.

prophets."[1] Still the fourth gospel quotes him as saying: "A new commandment I give unto you, That ye love one another; as I have loved you, that ye also love one another."[2] To explain this apparent contradiction I do not want to revert to the differences between Matthew and John, indisputable though they are. I think the words "as I have loved you" say what is new. Christians have at all times understood Jesus to have been the man who by his life has shown the actual possibility of perfect love; and this they mean by saying that the word of God has been made flesh. The Sermon on the Mount does not speak in the grammatical form of the imperative as does Moses' law; it does not say "Thou shalt not . . .", it speaks in the indicative: "Blessed are those who . . ." This is why the life of Christ is an integrating part of his word. I can evade a law, saying that I am not able to fulfil it. Can I evade the example of a life?

Judgment and hope have been close together even in the Jewish prophets. Historically the early prophets who spoke when the Jewish kingdom still existed spoke of the impending judgment; they had to destroy a false hope. The prophets at the time of the exile spoke of the impending hope, open to those who accepted the present judgment. This hope the Jews interpreted by expecting the Messiah who would restore the kingdom of David. The Christians said that this hope was now fulfilled, that Jesus was the Messiah; this is what the name Christ means. This is the same paradox as before. It is true it crushes the hopes of the Jews, for the visible kingdom of David has not been restored. Jesus himself has reinterpreted the idea of the coming kingdom: "The kingdom of God cometh not with observation: Neither shall they say, Lo here! or, lo there! for, behold, the kingdom of God is within you."[3] The words "within you" are probably a mistranslation, but a profound one, the original meaning being: "it is among you". In any case: it is here, you have no longer to wait for it.

[1] Matt. 22. 40. [2] John 13. 34. [3] Luke 17 20-1.

But if this were all that was to be said about the expectation, I should have spoken of fulfilment, not of hope. We have to learn that the words hope, judgment and fulfilment are ambiguous in the New Testament. John speaks clearly of the judgment as fulfilled in Christ: "He that believeth on him is not condemned; but he that believeth not is condemned already . . . And this is the condemnation, that light is come into the world, and men loved darkness rather than light . . ."[1] Equally clearly Matthew speaks of the coming judgment and the second coming of Christ.

This ambiguity seems to be inevitable. Christ has opened a way for every human person. To go or to miss it is that division between light and darkness, life and death, which is judgment. But if human persons are changed, history cannot stay unchanged. The fulfilment offered to the single person is the hope opened to mankind, the hope of history. This hope again means separation. "Think not that I am come to send peace on earth: I came not to send peace, but a sword. For I am come to set a man at variance against his father, and the daughter against her mother, and the daughter-in-law against her mother-in-law."[2] This is no longer the separation of one nation from all other nations. The separating line now goes through all nations and through all families. While the separation of the Jews from the other nations —whatever may have been the historical facts—was understood to have been effected at once, by the covenant of Sinai, this final separation is a process. In the parable of the tares among the wheat the servants ask whether they should gather up the tares but are forbidden by the householder "lest while ye gather up the tares, ye root up also the wheat with them. Let both grow together until the harvest: and in the time of harvest I will say to the reapers, Gather ye together first the tares, and bind them in bundles to burn them: but gather the wheat into my barn."[3] And Jesus, explaining the parable himself, says, according to the gospel: "the harvest is the end of the world". History will come to an end.

[1] John 3. 18-19. [2] Matt. 10. 34-5. [3] Matt. 13. 29-30.

With this expectation Christianity has entered history. Again and again Christians thought the last judgment to be close at hand. It never arrived, but history was steadily and incessantly transformed by those who waited for nothing but for its end.

As the first step of this transformation we may consider how the shattered hopes of the disciples, who had expected that Jesus would bring the judgment in his lifetime, were revived in a changed way by the report of his resurrection and by the profusion of the Holy Ghost seven weeks later. Whatever may have happened then, what they had wrongly expected to come immediately and from outside, they now knew as an overwhelming reality within themselves. From a broken sect they were transformed into a growing church.

They still expected the end to come soon, even during the life of many of them. This hope slowly withered away. Instead they conquered the Roman Empire from within in the span of three centuries. This success brought Christians into a dilemma of which the earliest church had had no idea and which, judging from the extant sources, does not seem to have been foreseen by Jesus himself. This dilemma has a conceptual as well as a practical side. We will be concerned mainly with the conceptual side. But since it can be made clear more easily in the practical field I shall first treat it there.

Consider any practical participation in what we call today political responsibility. Serving as a soldier in the Roman army may be a good example. The first Christians would certainly have considered this to be impossible for them. It is true that Jesus himself had shown great liberality toward the publicans who served the same state, and had accepted military obedience without any hesitation as an example for faith in his discourse with the Roman centurion. Still, killing, which belongs to the office of the soldier, must have seemed scarcely compatible with Christian love, or to put it more positively, with the Sermon on the Mount. Early Christians were not pacifists in a modern sense; they did not think of eliminating war by inducing everybody to live a peaceful life. But this was because they saw history as a battle between God and Satan that would come to an end soon, not by the efforts of man but by the power of God. The single Christian had to save his and his friends' souls, not to save the world. According to the predictions of the New Testament, especially of the Revelation of St. John, they even expected that the last act of human history would be the coming of Antichrist, a human ruler who would mock Christ by establishing an outward peace which would be the absolute dominion of evil. In this way they were aware of the ambivalence of the concept of peace, and for a long time the Roman Empire could be regarded by them as the impending fulfilment of this prediction, as what Babylon had been to the Jews. But if for a long time no Christian became a soldier it began to happen that soldiers became Christians. What should they do? Especially in the troubled 3rd century, when the Roman Empire began to decline, it could be argued that the soldier was defending peace and order and a chance to lead a godly life against the barbarians. Was not his service an act of brotherly love too? Indeed, when the choice was no longer between the Empire of Rome of this day and the Kingdom of Heaven which might begin tomorrow, but between the civilized Empire of Rome and the intruding Teutonic tribes and Parthian non-believers, the aspects began to change. How much more so after the Emperor had become a Christian.

Thus from the earliest centuries there is the tension between conservative and radical Christianity. There can be little doubt that the radical view is the earlier one. To it any attempt to help to preserve the existing order of things was a compromise with the pagan gods who now were considered demons of evil—an understanding, by the way, which seems at least more profound than that of a rationalism which denies their existence. On the other hand the conservative Christian would feel that by non-cooperation he might just have saved his conscience in too easy a way. A truly sovereign attitude like that expressed in the

Epistles of St. Paul was probably able at all times to find positive solutions to the concrete questions of the day, which were neither narrowly conservative nor narrowly radical. But whoever has had to face decisions of this kind himself in our days knows how far we are from knowing these answers easily or in advance.

The result of Christian history under these auspices could not be anything but ambivalent. Wheat and tares were growing together. Let us first consider the wheat. We may doubt how much better the late Roman and the Byzantine Empires may have been than earlier empires by being Christian. But at least when in St. Benedict and in Pope Gregory the Great the most radical tradition of Christian life, monasticism, merged with the best Roman tradition of firm and wise government, the foundations for a new age were laid in the midst of the breakdown of antiquity. From those days the church had the responsibility for feeding the poor. In order to be equal to this task it had to cultivate rotten and virgin lands. It had to pacify barbaric rulers. Bishops became preservers of stable government. Monks carried the tradition of ancient culture through the dark ages. What we call Europe is the making of Christianity.

But a price had to be paid for this achievement. Did bishops ruling a land convert the state or pervert Christianity? Were not pride, riches, and violence the attributes of Christian rulers as they had been of pagan lords? This is human, after all; and their faults were often tempered by the understanding of every Christian that love of the neighbour was the real criterion by which human behaviour was to be measured, and that the king was not divine but under God. But was not this acceptance of a tempered human nature just an act of treason against the superhuman hope opened by Christ to the human race? Was it really true and tested, that violence could not be avoided and that the church had to be rich; could pride be a good thing under any circumstances? The expectation of the last judgment was kept alive by comparing the teaching of the gospel with the world within which Europeans actually lived.

Let us leave the political scene for a while and turn to the development of concepts, of Christian thought.

In earliest times, when the second coming of Christ was expected from day to day, no consistent self-interpretation of Christianity may have been needed. The gospel told itself from mouth to mouth, from heart to heart. But even this is an abstraction. The gospel was told in a language which had been there before the gospel, and there is no language that would not carry with it an implicit philosophy. Our first written document, the New Testament, is full of interpretation. Probably the need of explicit interpretation, indicating the new awareness of this problem, was the reason why the New Testament was written. Matthew is a Jewish interpretation, John not far from a gnostic one, and in the Acts and in Paul's Epistles we see how a Hellenistic interpretation was arising. As Christianity was discussed and accepted by people belonging to the educated upper class of the Empire, interpretation in terms coined by Greek philosophy became its destiny. The most important school of philosophy in later antiquity was Neo-Platonism, which perhaps may be called a re-interpretation of Platonism in a religious mood and with concepts influenced by Hellenistic, mainly Stoic thought. Thus Christian philosophy or theology—the two were not yet separated—was of a Neo-Platonic character during its first thousand years. Is this fact not also subject to the parable of the wheat and the tares? Yet: how are we to distinguish wheat and tares?

In those times the *Timaeus* came to be considered Plato's most important work. Plato would certainly not have thought it to be so himself. He wrote many books about questions which in his view admitted of a certain answer or which were important for leading a life worthy of human beings: on the theory of the forms, on ethics, on political order. A cosmogony he wrote just once in his life-time and he called it no more than a likely story; he had to show that at least he was able to do better in this field, explaining the world by reason, than the Atomists had done explaining it by blind chance. But now the theological setting of this myth came to be considered as some premonition of the truth revealed in the holy scriptures of the Christians, while the science to which his epistemology refers was no longer understood and his model of a city-state governed by philosophers was as far from reality, being a city-state, as it was from the eschatological hopes, being of this world. In the early middle ages Plato was transformed into some kind of a Greek Moses; and Moses, in an equally unhistorical manner, was thought to have been the author of Genesis.

I want at least to mention the views about creation, held by the, probably, greatest Christian thinker of that first millennium, St. Augustine, as he expounds them in the three last books of his *Confessions* and elsewhere. It is characteristic of the interpretative character of this Christian philosophy that even a thinker as original and as impetuous as St. Augustine offers his views about this subject in an interpretation of a given text which here is the first chapter of Genesis. This interpretation of course lacks all the considerations about the real history of the text which are so characteristic of Biblical scholarship since the nineteenth century and of which I have made use in my third lecture. To St. Augustine the text of Genesis I is the word of God, dictated to Moses. Much of the interpretation is allegorical, much of it is devoted to his own profound philosophical thought, e.g. to his completely fresh and original analysis of the concept of time. As an example of the allegorical interpretation I should mention that the Firmament of Heaven is understood to indicate the firm authority of Scripture and the lights in Heaven to indicate the saints. To our understanding this is very far from the clear and simple meaning of the original text; in a philosophy, however, in which every created thing somehow symbolizes God's creative will as, to use Platonic language, the copy symbolizes the archetype, allegory must seem a natural way of interpretation.

Some of the speculative statements made by St. Augustine are that God created the world out of nothing and that he did not create the world in time but that he created time with the world.

The assertion of a creation out of nothing is the final stage of the development of thought which I described in the lecture on the Old Testament, asserting God's omnipotence. A pre-existent material of the world would seem not to have been the work of God, hence somehow not subject to him. Here a clear stand is taken against Plato and for the rational consequences of the Bible. The origin of evil, in St. Augustine's philosophy, is not in pre-existent matter but in the free decision of created souls. How this combines with his views on predestination is a question that would lead us too far from our present topic.

The other statement, that God did not make the world in time, is one of St. Augustine's own profound speculations. If the world has had a beginning, contrary to the prevailing view of Greek philosophy, what did God do before the creation? Why did he create the world in the moment in which he actually did rather than in any other moment? Such were the questions by which a philosophically trained pagan might try to expose the naive mythology of the Christian belief in creation. St. Augustine considers worth quoting, although he rejects it, the malicious answer: "He made hells for those who pry into mysteries." In fact, there is no answer to the question; we must understand that the question itself is wrongly put. God's own existence is not in time, his existence is absolute presence, not admitting of concepts like past and future. In this connection St. Augustine analyses flowing time as human beings know it, more thoroughly and in a far more modern-looking way than any ancient philosopher. But this analysis is used to show that this concept of time does not apply to God. God is not in time but he made time when he made the world. Even the expressions "he made" and "when he made" give the human aspect of creation, the aspect in flowing time, and hence not God's aspect.

We have still to consider the transformation of Plato's theory of forms in this Christian philosophy. The Form of the Good was the highest element in the hierarchy of Plato's thought. Sensual things are not truly being. The forms are truly being.

The form of forms is even beyond being, as he explicitly says. This is the origin of the later concept of transcendence. The forms are the archetypes according to which the *demiourgos* makes the sensible world; he has not made the forms, he only sees them as they are and ever have been. Now the God of the Christians is on the highest level. A person now takes the place of the impersonal Form of the Good, and the divine artisan is re-interpreted as being identical with him. What, then, are the forms? They are God's creative ideas according to which he made the world. The realm of ideas is God's infinite intellect. This is the beginning of the transformation which ended in the modern subjective use of the word "idea". Plato's idea is sheer or, as we would say "objective", existence. St. Augustine's idea is God's thought. Man, made in God's image, can think God's thoughts once more, though in a finite manner. Thus the idea is rightly understood to be in the mind of human persons too. In modern times this last use of the word idea is the only thing that is left. In Locke's view the idea still somehow represents things as they are. But when this is no longer confirmed by God's ideas, even the relation of ideas to things becomes doubtful, and in the end even the meaning of the view that there is to be such a relation. This question is to be treated in the second series of lectures.

Let us turn to the beginning of the second millennium of Christian thought. In the 13th century the philosophy of Aristotle was received by Christian thinkers, being delivered to them by the Arabs and the Jews. The theology and philosophy of St. Thomas Aquinas is the most famous attempt to harmonize Aristotle with Christianity. With respect to the ideas on creation not much seems to have been changed thereby. Still, St. Thomas had to state explicitly that the creation of the world in time—as we say—is a revealed truth, not a truth that can be proved by the natural light of reason. In fact if reason is embodied in the philosophy of Aristotle this is clear, since Aristotle states that the world is everlasting.

What is interesting to us in these statements is not so much their contents as the distinctions by which they are expressed. The natural light of reason is distinguished from revelation, philosophy is distinguished from theology. These distinctions which come so naturally to a person brought up in the occidental tradition of thought are not at all obvious. They are in fact a self-explanation of a culture which had to interpret the truth belonging to one tradition of thought by the conceptual means belonging to another tradition. If we look at the actual use of the words we shall find reason to mean Greek philosophy and revelation to mean the Bible. Philosophy is what is acceptable of Greek thought to Christians; theology is an interpretation of Biblical thought. The distinction of reason and revelation is present already in the Fathers, i.e. in those Christian thinkers who still belong to the ancient civilization. The distinction of theology and philosophy has developed in the rising culture of medieval Europe; it is particularly apt to reconcile Aristotle with Christianity.

What does the advent of Aristotelianism mean? Look at Raphael's *School of Athens*. Plato's lifted forefinger points to Heaven, Aristotle's outspread hand leads our view towards the earth. This is not a precise description of the true nature of the two great Greeks, but it gives an accurate picture of what the middle ages thought of them. Aristotelianism means reason instead of ecstasy, it means a positive, though relative valuation of the senses instead of their rejection. The advent of Aristotelianism announces that an age of science is to come. This historical fact has been completely distorted by the anti-Aristotelian self-interpretation of the next great step towards science which was taken in the 17th century. As I said before, the tradition of Christian thought has been interpretative. This was partly due to the prominence of a Sacred Book, partly to the fact that for centuries the newly-formed European nations, rather like schoolboys, had to learn a great deal from ancient cultural traditions. Thus even the daring attempt towards their own ways of thought which goes on through the high middle ages had to assert itself by establishing new authorities rather than by rejecting all authority.

The last question I am going to ask in this lecture is: what is the meaning or the origin of this new interest taken in reality? In so speaking I already use modern language. More correctly I should say: the new interpretation of the meaning of reality? To Christian Neo-Platonism God had been the one great reality. St. Augustine is concerned about God and the soul, nothing else matters. Nothing else? he asks himself. Nothing else, is the answer. The importance attached to a thing and the reality ascribed to it go close together. To the moderate conceptual realism of St. Thomas the form of a thing, that is its participation in the universal, is its true reality, yet it is concrete only in consisting of form and matter. To later nominalism only the individual thing has real existence. This has become the modern concept of reality. For the final part of this lecture I shall use this concept of reality in a terminological manner: Modern man is concerned about reality; modern language honours a man by calling him a realist.

The average modern self-interpretation is that this concept of reality has been wrought from religious prejudice. This makes modern times appear like a new civilization, different from the other-worldly civilization of the middle ages. Since giving up the Christian tradition is not acceptable to everybody, Christianity is then re-interpreted as some moral code of a very high standard; this is a form in which it seems to refer to reality in the modern sense. Certainly this understanding reveals important aspects of Christianity; still I think it is a misinterpretation of the inner dynamics of the Christian faith. In the field of theoretical thought I shall treat of this question in the following lectures. I want to make clear its practical background in the final remarks of this lecture.

Let us return once more to the ambivalence of Christian history. As I said, history was steadily and incessantly transformed by those who waited for nothing but for its end. Let us follow this transformation through the middle ages and the beginnings of modern times. Bishops had become preservers of stable government. This was a great success of the Christian attack on unbridled nature. But taking part in government they were in a situation similar to that of feudal barons; for a long time they had to come from aristocratic families themselves. They served the king against disorder; they were even invested by the king or the emperor. But they did not belong to the Church? The Pope as the head of the Church, it was felt, ought to have invested them. And is noble birth a necessary attribute of him who is to love his brethren as the carpenter's son had done? Thus what was acceptable to one century seemed inadmissible to the next one. Christianity means a steady movement of aggression against the prevailing state of affairs.

The middle ages can be understood as being a sequence of Christian reform movements like that of Cluny and that of the Franciscans. The Pope won his century-long fight against the Emperor. But the Emperor-like Pope then succumbed to what was probably an alliance of spirituality in the Christian sense and reality in the modern sense. The medieval church had tried to establish an order that was spiritual in its origin and of this world in its effect. When nearly established it was no longer convincing spiritually to those who tried to be radical Christians; at the same time it seemed insupportable to the smaller rulers of this world. The Pope had already overcome the Emperor because of a similar alliance; the feeling of many good Christians that the Pope had higher spiritual legitimacy than the Emperor to establish a Christian order in this world was mingled with the wishes of feudal barons in Germany and of modern-minded city-states in Italy to establish their own power. When the French king carried the Pope to Avignon the universal aspirations of the Pope had become as dubious as those of the Emperor had been a hundred years earlier.

I shall try to describe this threefold battle by means of three abstract concepts: nature, Christianity, and reality. I do not use these concepts now in their full and ordinary meaning; I use them to describe forces active in history in words they themselves used. In the time of which I speak the feudal baron may represent nature most clearly, the Franciscan friar may stand for Christianity, and the merchant citizen of a city, say an early Medici of Florence, may stand for reality. I am not certain whether I would be able to define these concepts very clearly although I feel those who know history will have an intuition of their meaning.

"Nature" is intended to indicate those established patterns of life and those forces in the human mind which were there before Christianity came to them. The word "nature" is taken from the Christian vocabulary; it means natural man who needs salvation. Nature would express itself largely in the language of myth. I think this concept applies well to the early feudal society of the European nations, while its application to the old civilization of pre-Christian antiquity would be unsatisfactory.

Christianity I have tried to explain in this lecture. It understood itself as representing a supernatural power; in fact it attacked the ways of life of nature. In order that charity should act in a person the powers which naturally dominate the soul must be overcome; they must, in fact, be slain like the early gods of the myths. Nobody likes to love his neighbour, not as we think he ought to be but as he really is. This is what the fourth gospel indicates by the words "except a corn of wheat fall into the ground and die, it abideth alone; but if it die, it bringeth forth much fruit".[1] God delivers us from the hands of the gods.

Reality, or more clearly secularized reality, is a word by which I try to describe the world which is delivered from the gods without belonging to the God of charity. It is the world of the autonomy of man. The hypothesis about our history which I want to bring forth here is that reality in this sense has only been made possible by Christianity. I first expressed this view when I

[1] John 12. 24.

said in the third lecture: God himself has deprived the world of its divinity. In order to give a considered judgment about this hypothesis we will have to go through the next four lectures; I shall return to the question in the last lecture of this series. Now I can only try to point to the developments in history in which similar acts appear first in a Christian and then in a secular form. I shall limit these brief remarks to three phenomena: obedience, government, and revolution.

The strictest form of obedience known to most people of our days is in military discipline. The strictest form of obedience which probably has ever existed in history was in monastic orders. St. Ignatius Loyola invented the much quoted dictum that the monk should be submitted to his superior like a corpse which makes no movement of his own. What does that mean to a Christian? The superior is to be considered the representative of God to whom really all obedience is due; the eradication of one's own subjective will is the death of the corn of wheat. I think the military orders of knights brought this concept of obedience to the military field where in feudal times discipline was far from being strict. The Spanish and Prussian soldiers came from countries whose medieval history had been largely a history of knightly orders. How far monastic and military obedience really have led towards inner freedom, is one of the many questions pointing to the ambivalence of our history. We leave it here unanswered, but we must return to it in the end.

Orderly government was promoted by bishops, as I said before. Modern political history is partly the history of an increasing power of the state. What the state subdues is precisely that magnificently unbridled nature which was so strongly represented in the feudal baron. By the 16th century in England, and the 17th century in French history the king had taken over the promotion of this development; the divine right of kings then was the modern idea versus feudalism. Equality of law and functioning of the state are a heritage left to democracy by absolutism. Later the abstract concepts of state and government take over the rôle of the king. The modern democratic state is even more powerful in executing its intentions than absolute monarchy was, and precisely for this reason the legal impediments against misuse of power are so important today.

But if government may in this sense be radical when in process of being established, it tends to become conservative after its establishment. What I called conservative Christianity may now be described as Christianity compromising with nature. Then Christian radicalism, if understood politically, tends towards revolution. Cromwell's Puritans considered the divine right of kings un-Christian, and so did the French Revolution, using the classical Christian concepts of liberty, equality, fraternity in a secular sense. This transformation of Christian radicalism into the radicalism of reality I should like to describe by the concept of secularization, using this term in a pregnant sense.

Now I leave political history for the space of four lectures.

6 *Copernicus, Kepler, Galileo*

In 1543 Nicolaus Copernicus published his book *De revolutionibus orbium coelestium* in which he announced what is now known as the Copernican system. The sun, according to this system, is at rest near the centre of the universe. The earth, on the other hand, has a double motion: it is rotating around its own axis in 24 hours and revolving around a point near the sun in one year.

This system had been known to Greek astronomy. It had been known and rejected. Aristarchus of Samos in the 3rd century BC seems to have put it in a shape most similar to that it received by Copernicus. Hipparchus, who lived about a hundred years later, and who is regarded as the greatest observer in ancient astronomy, rejected it. He offered another interpretation of planetary motion which was later known as the Ptolemaic system, getting its name from Ptolemy of Alexandria who about AD 150 wrote the classical textbook on ancient astronomy. If we want to understand modern astronomy it will be useful first to learn why, probably, the Greeks rejected what we think to be the correct system although they knew it and understood it very well.

That the earth is at rest is certainly the most natural view, if we start from everyday experience. But then the sky seems to be at rest too, and the earth seems to be a flat disk. As I said when speaking of the atomists, Greek science had abandoned these naive and natural views at an early time. The earth was recognized to be a sphere, surrounded by the sky as a sphere concentric with that of the earth. Since the stars including the sun, and less accurately, also the moon, complete their diurnal motions without an appreciable change of their relative positions it is a good starting point to think of them as fixed to the sphere of the sky. If we accept that, one thing is certain: there is a motion of the sky relative to the earth; one rotation is completed within 24 hours. But then the question may be asked: Is the earth at rest and the sky moving around it, or is the sky at rest and the earth turning within it? Or are both moving, perhaps? Their relative motion is the only thing we can see; what is the absolute motion?

Greek astronomers and philosophers were quite aware of this question. Several views were held; the final decision in which Aristotle and Ptolemy agree is that the earth is at rest. The main reason for this decision came from physics. The Greeks knew the size of the earth quite well. Hence they knew that the required motion of the earth—if we make the assumption that the sky is at rest—would have been more than 300 yards per second in the geographic latitude of Greece. Bodies which move far slower than that begin to tumble and you feel the oncoming air like a strong wind. In fact, the earth, moving with the speed mentioned, would go along under the air as under a terrible storm. Even more refined questions can be asked, e.g.: If you drop a stone from a high tower would it not fall down westward from the point vertically below the point where you dropped it; since while the stone is falling the earth has been moving on to the east? It is easy from a modern point of view to answer that the earth carries air, falling stones and everything with it. This idea had of course occurred to Greek thinkers as well. But they did not yet know the law of inertia, they did not even have an abstract concept of laws of nature. To them a body on which no force acts stays at rest. Hence they would have had to find out forces which can move thin air and freely falling stones with the earth. A force always meant a moving thing that exerted the force, if possible a moving thing contiguous with the moved one (just like the physicists of the 17th and 20th centuries AD the Greeks did not believe in action at a distance). You see easily that the famous principle, mostly quoted as "Occam's razor" by modern English-speaking empiricists, the principle of not introducing more entities than necessary, was applied most sensibly by those Greeks who rejected the diurnal motion of the earth. Then, of course, they faced the question how the sky stands the stress of its far faster motion. But after all, the sky certainly consists of a material very different from all materials we know; its fast motion is only an additional wonderful quality added to the luminosity of its stars, to its evident lightness, and to its perfect circular shape.

But the real astronomical problem arose with the annual motion. To say that the sky moves as a whole is only a first approximation. Most stars, it is true, are fixed to it and are called fixed stars for that reason. But there are seven stars which wander their own paths between the others; these paths are not easily predicted and the seven stars are therefore rightly called planets, that is erratic stars. Five of them look like ordinary stars, though uncommonly bright and with a steady, untwinkling light: Mercury, Venus, Mars, Jupiter, Saturn. You see they bear the names of gods. The moon is to be added to them, wandering around the heavenly sphere within one month. The sun, too, is a planet. You cannot see the stars in its neighbourhood because of its own light, but at night you see what stars stand on the side of the sky opposite to the sun, and they change with the seasons. Hence it is easily seen that the year is just the period of one revolution of the sun.

As I said, the motions of the planets are somewhat erratic. They keep fairly well to one great circle on the sphere of heaven which is called the zodiac or the ecliptic. There again they wander on the average in the same direction but with different speeds, the moon revolving around the sky once in a month, Saturn once in 29 years. But besides that the five star-like planets act at certain times like dancers. They stop, turn backwards, complete a loop and go forward again. Thus Mercury and Venus dance around the sun; therefore Venus appears at times as morning star and at times as evening star, but never at midnight. Mars, Jupiter and Saturn move independently. But they make their loop once every year, precisely when their position in the sky is opposite the sun. Thus, in a way, the sun seems to be governing all the planetary motions.

How are we to explain that? Greek astronomers tried to give a rigorous mathematical theory which would explain or, as they used to say, save the phenomena. I omit the very ingenious earlier systems like that of 27 spheres rolling within each other, invented by Eudoxus. Aristarchus offered the Copernican solution. The sun is at rest in the centre of the system. In that sense it is not a planet but the governing body of the world. Its apparent annual motion is really a motion of the earth which revolves around the sun in one year. The earth is a planet like the other planets. The moon is a satellite of the earth, just moving around it without further complications. The five remaining star-like planets move around the sun. Mercury and

Venus are closer to the sun than the earth. Hence they will never be seen at a great distance from the sun if they are observed from the earth. The three other planets are farther away from the sun than the earth. Hence there are times, roughly once a year, when the earth is situated between them and the sun. Seen from the earth they will then be located opposite to the sun. The earth is moving faster than the outer planets. Hence during these times when they are opposite the sun they must seem to move backwards to an observer who lives on the earth. I remember how, when I was a little child, I sat for the first time in a motor car and how surprised I was to see the trees of the roadside moving away from us with great speed. In fact, the loops in the apparent motions of the outer planets are inverted images of the annual motion of the earth around the sun. A slow advancement, superimposed on recurring loops, is precisely the relative motion between two bodies circling around the same centre at different speeds. Thus the explanation of the observed facts by this theory is excellent; more than that, we are accustomed to say in modern times that it is true.

But the Ptolemaic system is by no means inferior to the Copernican in explaining the apparent motions as far as I have described them. To the modern mind this can be made clear most easily by using the concept of relative motion. First consider the relative motion of the sun and the earth only. Aristarchus and Copernicus say that the sun is at rest and the earth revolves around it in a well-defined circle. There is no difficulty in assuming it to be the other way round, the earth being at rest and the sun being carried around in an exactly corresponding circle. Then imagine that the relative motions of the other five planets with respect to the sun are the same as in the Copernican system. But since now the sun is considered as moving, all the other planets will be carried around with the sun in addition to their own motion around the sun. Thus the five planets now have a double motion: around the sun and with the sun. The aspects of their orbits as seen from the earth will not be changed thereby; for the motion of the outer planets, i.e. with the sun, is seen from the earth as their annual loop, while their motion around the sun is interpreted in the Ptolemaic system as being the progression of the point around which they perform the loop. What we can observe, as long as we lack an absolute frame of reference, are only relative motions, and they are identical in the two systems.

Now this is a very modern way of describing the question (the specialists would say that I interpreted Tycho's system in a relativistic manner, thus proving that a geocentric system, if adequately formulated, cannot be refuted by purely kinematic considerations at all). Greek and early modern astronomers used rather different terms, and hence they could think that there were real differences between the two systems. For instance, Ptolemy would of course not have taken the Copernican system as a starting-point, transforming it into his own by a change of the frame of reference. He started out assuming the earth at rest. The double motion of an outer planet then was described by saying that there is a circle around the earth on which an ideal point moves; and this ideal point is the centre of another circle, the so-called epicycle, on which the planet itself revolves. Thus the motion of the planet is like the motion of a point on the circumference of a little wheel.

I have so far always spoken of circles. In the modern view this is only approximately true; a better approximation is to speak of ellipses which are not very eccentric. But to ancient astronomy as well as to Copernicus it was a sacred truth that heavenly bodies had to move in exact circles. The circle was the most perfect line, and heavenly bodies were the most perfect bodies; in some views they were in fact held to be divine or angelic entities. Nobody in our time can imagine what a sacrilegious impossibility it would have been to assume these perfect bodies to move in an imperfect way. This forced restrictions upon those astronomers that made their systems less flexible than they might have been. Ptolemy had to compromise a great deal. In fact he composed his orbits from two superimposed circular motions.

Further, he admitted that the centres of the circles of the planets were not in the sun, but in different places not far from the sun. Finally he had even to give up the idea of a constant angular velocity of the planet in its circle. All this was done in order to save the phenomena. It was the complication so well known to every scientist which arises when you try to adapt a theory, in which something is basically wrong, to carefully observed facts. But what was wrong was equally wrong in Copernicus and in Ptolemy; it was the veneration of the circle.

This, then, leads us back to the question: Why did the Greeks finally prefer Ptolemy, and why did the Moderns prefer Copernicus?

There are two arguments in favour of Ptolemy. The one is that the motion of the earth around the sun would have seemed quite as difficult to reconcile with physics as its motion around its own axis. The second is that if the earth moves, its true motion should be reflected not only in the apparent motions of the planets—the "loops"—but also in an apparent motion of the fixed stars. Nothing of the kind was observed. It is true, if you move on a road with high speed, neighbouring trees seem to move in the opposite direction very fast, but a distant mountain range will not change its apparent position for a long time. Thus, if the fixed stars do not reflect the motion of the earth they must be very far away. Today we know that the nearest fixed star is at a distance from the sun nearly 300,000 times the distance of the earth from the sun which, in its turn, is about 100 million miles. Again Occam's razor can be invoked: Why introduce enormous distances if it is not necessary? And in Ptolemy's system where the earth is at rest no reflection of a motion in the fixed stars is expected. The empirical proof of the existence of this reflected motion in the fixed stars was not produced before the middle of the 19th century.

Having understood these good scientific reasons which favour Ptolemy we will no longer wonder why the Copernican system was but slowly accepted in modern times. We may rather wonder why it was accepted at all. There were good astronomical reasons arising from more exact observations and from new theories on physics; I shall come to them immediately. But they were discovered by men who believed in Copernicus even before they had discovered them. I think what made Copernicus so attractive to people like, say, Kepler, Galileo, and Descartes, was in the beginning a psychological fact. The discussions that may have taken place among Greek astronomers were forgotten; Ptolemy was nearly all that was known. Ptolemaic astronomy and Aristotelian philosophy had become an entrenched, dogmatic system of thought, very different from the mood in which Aristotle or Hipparchus themselves had done their exciting researches. The Copernican system came as a completely new, original idea, daring to do away with the humbug of traditions; to accept it meant that men were then free to think about nature by themselves. New observations were made. They fitted in with the Copernican system very well. It was not always attempted to fit them into the Ptolemaic system equally well. (Tycho, it is true, tried precisely that.) Ptolemy's system had become rather rigid, not so much owing to its essential structure as to its having been considered as true for so many centuries. Even a truth can be distorted by being publicly recognized for centuries; how much more so a still doubtful hypothesis. Thus the quiet revolutions of the planets around the sun offered the key-word of modern times, though in a very different sense: the word revolution.

It may be argued that the truly revolutionary discovery in modern theoretical astronomy was not the Copernican system but Kepler's first law (1604). Kepler states that planets move in ellipses, the sun being situated in one focus of the ellipse. This discovery was made possible by the restless observations of Tycho Brahe. It was one of the lucky accidents in the history of science that the treasure of these long lists of numbers assembled during twenty years of unceasing work by the great Danish observer was entrusted to the hands of a scientific genius full of imagination, and at the same time scrupulous in the slightest detail, and of unswerving industry, like Johannes Kepler. Kepler believed in the mathematical perfection of the celestial spheres perhaps more intensely than any man before or after him has done. For that very reason he was not prepared to leave unexplained a difference less than eight minutes of arc between the theoretical and the observed motions of the planet Mars. Eight minutes of arc is the fourth part of the apparent diameter of the moon; this small distance between the predicted and the observed position of a planet had to be accounted for. Kepler sacrificed the idea of the circles after more than forty assumed theoretical orbits of Mars had failed to agree sufficiently well with the observations. He tried the ellipse as a working hypothesis, and he was struck by the discovery that it fitted the observations precisely. He then had enough mathematical imagination to think that an ellipse might be an element of a perfect system of celestial motions as well as a circle.

I am not going to describe here Kepler's elaborate ideas about the harmony of the spheres. They are a work of mathematical art, perhaps somehow resembling Bach's *Kunst der Fuge*; but they are not science in the modern sense and thus, in spite of their beauty, they are well and perhaps rightly forgotten. I want to ask another question: What has all that to do with cosmogony?

Since astronomy tries to describe the all-embracing structure of our world it seems natural that it should be the science predestined to produce cosmogonical theories. In fact, however, neither ancient nor early modern astronomy is in any known way connected with cosmogony. In antiquity I had to speak of philosophy when introducing cosmogonical theories, and even in modern times we will encounter cosmogony first in the ideas proposed by two philosophers: Descartes and Kant. Yet this is understandable. A precise observation of the motion of planets revealed only periodic movements without the slightest hint of an evolution, a growth or a decay, or any irreversible change.

Mechanical causality seemed as remote from the celestial bodies as biological growth; heaven looked like a great finished work of art. The possibility of describing it in terms of invariable mathematical rules rendered its difference from all we know on earth even more striking, since everything under the moon is changing fast and in different ways from day to day. To Kepler astronomy was an adoration of the Creator by the medium of mathematics. In mathematical laws man, made in God's image, rethinks God's creative thought. This is the world of Timaeus and not of Democritus.

The necessary step before a scientific cosmogony could be tried was to bring heaven and earth together under the domination of common laws of physics. Mathematics had to be brought down to earth, mechanics up to heaven. This was done by the establishment of the science called celestial mechanics. This in its turn was achieved in three phases. Celestial motions had to be described exactly in mathematical terms: this was achieved by Kepler. Mechanics had to be established as a mathematical science; this was mainly done by Galileo. Mechanics had to be applied to celestial motions; this was Newton's crowning work.

Speaking of Galileo Galilei I want to discuss two topics: his achievements in mechanics, and his fight for the Copernican system. In both fields I am more interested now in the questions of principle than in the details, which the interested reader can find in any sufficiently modern history of science.

By establishing the science of mechanics, Galileo brought mathematics down to the earth. In this he followed another great Greek thinker, Archimedes, whom he greatly admired. What Archimedes had done for statics he wanted to do for dynamics, for the theory of motion. This theory he did not leave to posterity in perfected form; later physicists, mainly Huygens and Newton, and even the great mathematicians of the 18th century, had still to add a great deal. Still, the decisive mental effort may be said to have been Galileo's. Let us try to understand this mental effort.

Modern science has an historical myth of its own. It is the myth of Galileo. This myth asserts that in the dark ages the speculations of Aristotle, unfounded on observation, were held in high esteem, but that Galileo broke the path for science by describing the world as we really experience it. Like every myth, this myth expresses some truth; certainly it is right in its very high valuation of Galileo. But I think that it completely distorts the nature of Galileo's real achievement. I should try to describe his achievement by saying exactly the opposite of the myth. Hence I say: The late middle ages are in no way dark ages, they are a time of high culture, bristling with intellectual energy. They adopted Aristotle because of his concern about reality. But the main weakness of Aristotle was that he was too empirical. Therefore he could not achieve a mathematical theory of nature. Galileo took his great step in daring to describe the world as we do not experience it. He stated laws which in the form in which he stated them never hold in actual experience and which therefore cannot be verified by any single observation but which are mathematically simple. Thus he opened the road to a mathematical analysis which decomposes the complexity of actual phenomena into single elements. The scientific experiment is different from everyday experience in being guided by a mathematical theory which poses a question and is able to interpret the answer. It thereby transforms the given "nature" into a manageable "reality". Aristotle wanted to preserve nature, to save the phenomena; his fault was that he made too much use of common sense. Galileo dissects nature, teaches us to produce new phenomena; and to strike against common sense with the help of mathematics.

Take any simple example. Aristotle says that heavy bodies fall fast, light bodies fall slowly, very light bodies will even rise. This is exactly what everyday experience teaches us; a stone will fall fast, a sheet of paper more slowly, a flame will even rise. Galileo says that all bodies fall with equal acceleration and will therefore after equal time have acquired equal velocity. In everyday experience this is just wrong. Galileo goes on to tell us that in a vacuum bodies would really behave like that. Here he states the hypothesis that there is a vacuum, an empty space, again contradicting not only Aristotle's philosophy but everyday experience. He was not able to produce a vacuum himself. But he greatly encouraged later 17th century physicists, like his pupil Torricelli, to make a vacuum; and in fact, when a sufficiently empty space was there, Galileo's prediction proved true. Further, his assertion opened the way for a mathematical analysis of buoyancy and friction, the two forces responsible for the different behaviour of falling bodies of different specific weights, sizes, and shapes. Only if you know how a body would fall without these forces will you be able to measure them by their impeding effect.

The same considerations hold for the law of inertia. It says that a body on which no forces are acting will keep its state of rest or of moving on in a straight line with unchanging speed. (I shall not consider here the complication that Galileo himself never stated the law clearly in this form, but still considered the apparently straight lines in true fact to be segments of large circles; very soon after him this complication was eliminated by his own pupils.) Nobody has ever seen a body moving on in a straight line with unchanging speed. Of course this is due to the fact that always some forces act on a body. Then the law of inertia gives us a chance to define clearly what we mean by a force; according to Newton the force is proportional to the acceleration of the body on which it acts. The acceleration is the change of the velocity vector per unit time. Hence the force is defined as proportional to the deviation of the body from its inertial path. But what a scrutinizing analysis and what an intellectual daring was needed before Galileo could express such a law which at the same time was not clearly visible in any phenomenon and was contrary to all traditional views of causality! It was an axiom that no change would happen without a cause producing and maintaining it. Motion is a change of position.

Hence there will be no motion without a cause, that is a force producing it. Now it is proposed that there is motion going on, though in the absence of any cause. Later thinkers like Descartes acquiesced in assigning a cause only to a change of state and defining the state of a body by its velocity. This is a clever trick; why did they not define the state by the position or the acceleration, or by the velocity of a constant circular motion? The law of inertia has its only justification in experience. Yet this experience is not present in any single case and certainly not in everyday experience. The empirical proof of the law is only in the comparison of the theory of mechanics as a whole with the realm of mechanical experiments as a whole.

I shall return to this epistemological problem in the second series of lectures. Now I want to point out only how this is connected with Platonism. Scientists of those times liked to invoke Plato against Aristotle in defence of their belief in mathematical laws. I think they were partly right in doing so. Compare the analysis of mathematics in Platonic terms which I tried to give in the fourth lecture. There we said: the true circle is not to be found in this world of the senses. Equally we can now say: the true inertial motion is not to be found in this world of the senses. True science must needs transcend what the senses tell us. But there the strict analogy comes to an end. To Plato only pure mathematics has any claim to be called true cognition, the real claim being reserved for the philosophical theory of the forms; of the sense world nothing more than a likely story can be told. To Galileo mathematical law holds strictly in nature and it can be discovered by an effort of the human mind which includes the performing of experiments. Nature, being complicated, does not always offer us the simple cases in which the one law we want to study is free from disturbances. But these disturbances, being caused by forces that obey their own laws, are equally open to mathematical study. Go on dissecting nature and you will be its master. The realism of modern science is neither a naive belief in the senses nor is it an aloof spiritual disdain of them.

There is a theological background to this attitude. The world of the senses is the world of nature in the Christian sense of the word. Platonism and Christianity both rely on what is beyond nature. But there is the difference that Plato's God has not made matter; only the spiritual element in the world is divine; hence science, being a divine gift, does not apply to the material world in a strict sense. To Christians God has made everything. Hence man, made in his image, can understand all created things, that is, certainly the whole material world. The very idea that the Word has been made flesh, the dogma of Incarnation, shows that the material world is not too low to be accepted by God and hence to be understood by the light of reason given us by God. In his fight against the Inquisition for the Copernican system Galileo said clearly that we should read not only in the Book of Words given us by God for salvation but also in the Book of Nature given us by God in his creation.

But I want to speak about this famous fight in more detail. It has become another part of the Galilean myth. The myth says: "Galileo Galilei was a martyr for scientific truth versus medieval superstition." Again, this myth expresses some aspect of truth. Again it rightly emphasizes the key rôle played by Galileo. Again it distorts the historical facts to such a degree that one is tempted to express them by contradicting nearly every single word of the sentence in which I expressed the myth. But here the situation is even more involved. We shall see reasons for turning the tables more than once.

Was Galileo a martyr? Martyr means witness. So far we can agree. He was a public witness. He spoke publicly for science with great fervour and great literary skill, and he spoke for a theory which we believe to be true. If science and the Church are considered to be opponents, then it might be added that he was a witness in the sense that perhaps no single act has in the end done more harm to the Church—not only to the Roman

Church—than Galileo's trial; it is even now one of the main arguments of anti-Christian propaganda.

But the word martyr has come to mean a witness who openly professes his faith even when threatened with death and whose decisive testimony is in his death for his faith. Galileo was threatened with less than death—it is true, he was once probably threatened with torture and he was then seventy years old—and he abjured the Copernican theory under this pressure. If we use the word in the full sense, Galileo was not a martyr.

The historical fact is that Galileo did not become a martyr because he never wanted to be a martyr. He was a man of the late renaissance who enjoyed life and wanted to enjoy life, who enjoyed science and scientific fame and wanted to do so, and who was a good and faithful Catholic who never thought of conflict with his Church. Probably he was a good enough Catholic and a good enough scientist to understand clearly that martyrdom is testimony for religious and ethical beliefs and not for scientific truth. For religious and ethical beliefs refer to human actions and can only be testified by human actions; scientific beliefs refer to facts and can only be proved by looking into the facts. What he wanted to do was to convince his Church of a fact. He wanted to convince them that the Copernican view was true, was relevant, and was in no way contrary to the Catholic faith. He tried to achieve that by writing books, by making people look through telescopes, by talking privately to cardinals and to the pope. When his book was condemned he was prepared to amend it, and when he was forced to abjure he hated the people who had brought him into this situation and never spoke of them later otherwise than with cold contempt; but we have no indication that he doubted at any moment that, if diplomatic means could not save him, he would have to submit to the inevitable and to pronounce his abjuration. It is certain that he thought at that moment: *eppur si muove*—"and still the earth moves"; it is equally certain that he did not say it aloud, for he was no fool.

But why, then, did he not convince his Church? I am afraid

I must say: because he was not, after all, defending clear scientific truth against medieval backwardness. The situation was rather the opposite: he could not prove what he asserted, and the Church of his time was no longer medieval. To take the second point first: I think a modern biographer, G. de Santillana, is quite right in saying that the Roman Church of the early 17th century had gone so far on the way towards the modern totalitarian state that it could no longer admit of a latitude of thought which would have been possible in many medieval centuries and certainly in the renaissance. Galileo defended the then old-fashioned view that the dogmatic authority of the Church referred to those points which were relevant for salvation but not to conflicting views on nature. On the other hand, reading the documents of his trial I have had the impression that very few people in the Church were at all concerned whether he was really right or not. The Church was then rising from the blow of the Reformation; many doubtful questions of doctrine had been settled in the Council of Trent; the Jesuits had brought into the Church a far stricter idea of obedience; it was realized what strength the Church could gain from a monolithic adherence to dogma. The Thirty Years' War in Germany was going on. The Bible was God's word and it could not be easily reconciled with Copernicus—so why weaken the position of the Church in its fearful and perhaps final fight against the heretics by new internal quarrels on the motion of the earth? If we interpret it like that, the struggle between Galileo and the Inquisition was a struggle between two very modern powers: science and totalitarianism. Both sides believed in Christ, and probably each considered its side to represent the wheat, and the other side to represent the tares. Such is the ambivalence of history.

Each of the two sides was rather ambiguous in itself, and the opponent, with the keen eye of a clever adversary, saw its weakness, at least to some extent. Galileo's weakness in representing science was, as I said, that he could not prove his case scientifically. I have just to remind you of what I said about the Copernican system in the earlier parts of this lecture in order to show that this was so. It is true, in Galileo's hands the telescope had shown sunspots, mountains on the moon and a satellite system around Jupiter that looked like a minor model of Copernicus' idea of the planetary system around the sun. Thus some ancient beliefs about the celestial bodies had been shattered, mainly the idea that they were very different from the earth, consisting of a stainless heavenly material, but no conclusive scientific proof for or against Copernicus could be deduced from those matters. The strongest argument then existing might have been that Kepler's laws made sense in the Copernican system while their transformation into the language of Ptolemy would have been very awkward. But Galileo never used this argument; he does not seem even to have read Kepler's rather ill-written book on this subject although Kepler had sent it to him. The good theologians of the Church like Cardinal Bellarmine and the Jesuit astronomers (some of whom may have been Copernicans at heart) were of course aware of this situation. In the first so-called trial of 1615 in which Galileo was treated with great courtesy the official position of Bellarmine was that the Copernican system might well be used as a mathematical hypothesis for an easier description of the motions of the planets; only it could not be asserted as true, because there was no proof for it and because Scripture taught us that it was wrong. Hypothesis here evidently means an assumption in which we do not believe but which is useful for the simplification of calculations. Galileo submitted to this formula, but only as a *façon de parler*. He brought upon himself the final blow of the second real trial of 1633 by writing a book, his famous *Dialogues* on the two principal world-systems, in which he shielded his true opinion in too transparent a manner behind the language of this formula.

Thus we may even say that the Inquisition did not demand more from Galileo than that he should not say more than he could prove. He was the fanatic in this case. But we have now to turn the tables once more: he was right in being the fanatic. Science is not advanced by meticulously sticking to what we can prove. Science is advanced by daring assertions which open the ways of their own proof or disproof. All I said about falling bodies and the law of inertia exemplifies this statement, and we cannot doubt that Galileo was aware of this methodological situation. Science needs faith as well as religion, both faiths, if they understand their own position, submitting to their relative ways of testing: religious faith in human life, scientific faith in further investigations.

But if Galileo understood the nature of science better than the Inquisition, did he understand the rôle of science in history? He stood for what I have called the historical position of reality in the last lecture. Man is free to investigate the truth about nature. This freedom should not be impeded. But what about the consequences of the scientific findings? We must try to do justice to the motivations of the Church. If Galileo undermined the authority of the Bible and of 1500 years of Church tradition, where would this undermining stop? This authority may have been a cover for many bad things; but after all it had made Europe. If I attribute a bit more of clairvoyance to Cardinal Bellarmine than he probably had—must he not have shuddered, thinking of the consequences of the oncoming age of unbridled research? A straight way of three hundred years leads from classical mechanics to the mechanics of the atom. A straight way of twenty years leads from the mechanics of the atom to the atom bomb. Whether this bomb will destroy the western civilization by which it has been made is not yet clear. If you had been a Cardinal in 1615, and if you had seen the future till 1964, and not further, would you have dared to take the risk of this development if there was a hope of stopping it?

What the Church did not know was that there was no hope of stopping it. Here, I think, is the ambiguity in the position of the Church. I think it would be absolutely unjust to deny that its attempt to establish a system of authority that would prevent dangerous developments was prompted by a true sense of responsibility for mankind. Can those who know the dangers best do better for their brethren in this time in which we wait for the last judgment than by protecting them from evil by every means open to prudence? Has God willed that we should pry into the mysteries of his creation before he wants to open them to us in a new world?

This is precisely what I have called conservative Christianity in the last lecture. Stoic Roman Emperors, when they accepted the offerings brought to their person and meant by their contemporaries to acknowledge their beneficial rule as the least of evils, may have thought similarly. The political rule of the Church transferred the Roman Empire to the spiritual scene. But Christian radicalism had refused to submit to the Divine Emperor in the first centuries; by its apparently foolish insistence on adoring only the true God it had drawn upon itself persecutions and conquered the world. The radicalism of modern science now refused to submit to those men who had taken a divine responsibility into their human hands; even when scientists still were Christians they could not believe that it was a Christian attitude to submit to prudential considerations rather than to truth. Let the consequences of our search for truth rest in the hands of God. I think that in their insistence on truth early Christians and modern scientists have something in common, differently though they interpret the meaning of truth.

However this may be, the Church had to learn that even if the world of science contained the tares, it was not possible to gather up the tares before the harvest.

7 *Descartes, Newton, Leibniz, Kant*

THESE LECTURES have something like a circular structure. The general question about scientism led us to the question of the origin of scientism in history. For this narrower question I used Bentley's sermons and Kant's theory as a starting point. This brought me to the question of the relationship between myth and science, a question that induced me to take my starting point in history in the very early times of genuine myths. Having trodden the path of historical development we are to reach Bentley and Kant again in this lecture. Thus a first, greater circle will be closed today. But I shall pass by the meeting point, adding another smaller circle on the scientific cosmogony of our own time. It will lead us back to today's scientism, thereby transforming the travelled path into the shape of the figure 8.

To make a scientific cosmogony possible, heaven and earth had to be brought together under a common natural law. This was Newton's achievement. But as often happens, the question was first brought to the full consciousness of the *république des savants* by a premature answer. We must glance at this answer, which is the system of René Descartes.

Descartes offered an explanation of the planetary motions by his famous theory of the vortices. The planets are floating in an enormous eddy of very thin matter that moves around the sun. They are carried by it like pieces of cork in water.

This theory has the great advantage of answering precisely those questions about the celestial system which are not answered by Kepler's laws. According to Kepler's first law the planets move in ellipses, the sun occupying one focus of the ellipse. This leaves open two questions:

1. An ellipse can be nearly circular or very long-stretched or anything between these extremes. The orbits of the planets are not exact circles but very nearly so; their eccentricities are very small. Is there any reason for that?

2. Since the ellipse is a plane curve, the orbit of each planet defines a plane going through the sun. Kepler's law would not exclude these planes all stretching in different directions. Actually they are nearly identical. All planets move nearly in the same plane, and they all move in the same direction; they have the same axis and sense of revolution. The intersection of this common plane and the imaginary sphere of the sky is the great circle called the zodiac. Why do the planets follow this well-ordered pattern of motion?

In Descartes' view the explanation is obvious. The great eddy going around the sun has a unique axis of its rotation. The common plane of the planetary motions is the plane perpendicular to it and going through the sun. In this plane all the planets are carried in the same direction in the circular orbits prescribed by the eddying thin fluid in which they swim. Again, since these fluid motions are never quite precise, the slight deviations from the common plane and from the circular shape are not surprising.

This picture is not too different from the picture drawn by the Greek atomists 2000 years before Descartes. Their solid spherical sky, the "skin" as they called it, is now replaced by the fluid extending through space, in order to account for the known differences of distance of the planets from the earth; some assumption of this sort would have been necessary even to reconcile the view of the atomists with the Ptolemaic astronomy. Besides, the sun now takes the central position instead of the earth; Descartes is a Copernican, even if he uses diplomatically guarded language on this as on other dangerous points. But the eddy is there, the infinity of space is assumed again, and the fixed stars are understood to be suns similar to our own, surrounded by their own eddies, thus repeating the atomists' view that there is an infinite number of systems, or worlds, as they call them. Then, the atomistic cosmogony can easily be resumed. Eddies can slow down, new eddies can originate, as we see it in every flowing stream. Thus our system has arisen once out of a newly-formed eddy, and Descartes tries to describe this process in details that no longer interest us. That these processes can go on for ever is assured by a law of nature stated explicitly by Descartes: the quantity of motion in the universe is a constant. This law ought to be considered as an attempt to formulate a principle corresponding to what we call the conservation of energy; although Descartes, not yet possessing the correct laws of mechanics which were discovered by Huygens and Newton, after his time, formulated his principle in an untenable way.

Thus all the ingredients are ready for a world infinite in time in which cosmogony just means the origin of an ordered partial world like ours. The Christian concept of creation seems unnecessary if we do not want to say that God, being beyond time, created infinite time with the world. But Descartes tells us that the world has been made by God in time, and that God then gave it just that quantity of motion which is still present in it. He even says that he willingly submits to the teaching of the Church that God made heaven and earth and all the kinds of plants and animals individually within six days, and that his description of a different cosmogony only tends to show how God might have made the world in a different way, had he not chosen to do it as the Bible tells us. Here we easily recognize the diplomacy of a man who was resolved not to suffer Galileo's fate. The only difficulty is to know the boundary between his sincere views and his diplomacy. I think that he believed sincerely in God since he needed the philosophical concept of God, and that he considered the Church to be a necessary and useful institution, and that for these reasons he wanted not to attack but to convince the Church; but that he was not in any serious way concerned about Christ and about faith, hope, and charity, being a Stoic rather than a Christian. Whether or not he believed in an infinite duration of the universe, I am unable to say.

He was certainly sincere in another aspect of his system, and this aspect is modern in a strange manner. He thought he had done better than all his predecessors by having erected a strictly consistent system of thought of an intuitive clearness corresponding to that of mathematics. I can only indicate the structure of this system in a few sentences, using his cosmology as a starting point for an analysis that works backwards from the achieved system to its basic ideas.

Although his cosmology follows the atomistic pattern he denies the existence both of atoms and of empty space. Matter to him is continuous. Hence he claims to deduce the existence of the eddies; if continuous matter, which is described by him in terms that would correspond to the more recent concept of an incompressible fluid, is to move at all, the only motions which will not stretch into infinity recur in closed curves: they are eddies. That matter must be continuous follows from his denial of any distinction between matter and space; in his view matter and space are identical. This again follows from his view that nature can be described completely in terms of mathematics. The only discipline of pure mathematics that can be applied to extended things is geometry. Hence matter can have no properties besides the geometrical ones; matter is extension and nothing else. That nature should be described by mathematics again follows from the idea that all true knowledge must be clear and distinct, which is the case with mathematics but not with sense-perception. Only clear and distinct knowledge, in fact, is guaranteed to be true by the reliability of the all-wise and all-bountiful God who created us; assent to apparent knowledge that is not clear and distinct is a misuse of our free will. The existence of the all-perfect God can be proved strictly out of the existence of the idea of an all-perfect being which is present in my own mind, and this proof is necessary to overcome the doubt to which every belief can be subjected with the exception of my own existence, which is proved by my very doubting.

I shall not insist on the flaws in this deduction that have become more and more evident by the criticism of three subsequent centuries. Descartes' system will always remain important as the symbolic expression of modern man who is certain of nothing but of his ability to say "I" in a meaningful way, and who wants to assert his autonomy with respect to all existing things. He still needs the omnipotent God for his proof that science is trustworthy; but he no longer needs God within science. Nature is satisfactorily described by geometry.

But if we go on to the details that interest us here, the failure of this titanic attempt to do all the work of modern science in one man's life stands out in a pathetic manner. Descartes wanted to prove the truth of his system with mathematical rigour, and he was not even able to explain the one mathematical fact known about the planets in his time: Kepler's laws. The eddy explains why the planetary orbits are nearly circular, but it does not explain why they are precisely elliptical. Newton was able to explain precisely that, and hence he completely rejected Descartes' eddies.

I shall not repeat here the details of Newton's explanation of the planetary motions. In general terms they are well-known and in mathematical rigour they are not easy even for a physics undergraduate of our days. But I want to point out the conceptual structure of Newton's physics. If we want to explain any motion of bodies, like that of the planets, three things, according to Newton, must be known:

1. The general laws of motion.
2. A special law of force.
3. The particular initial conditions.

The general laws of motion have been given by Newton in the beginning of the *Principia*. The first law is the law of inertia, stating that a body which is not under the influence of a force will stay in its state of rest or of uniform rectilinear motion. The second law is Newton's most important own addition: the change of motion is proportional to the force. This law is not too easily interpreted, but I shall leave its inherent problems aside. In modern mathematical language it states that the force produces an acceleration proportional to it, the acceleration being defined as the second derivative of position with respect to time. Since the law of inertia has shown that no force is needed for a change of position, it is most natural to assume that the force causes the change of velocity, or, as Newton says, of the quantity of motion.

Evidently this general law will be of practical use only if we know the force acting on a given body. Here is Newton's second great contribution: the law of gravity. Gravitation is not the only force of nature, but according to Newton it is acting between any pair of bodies in the universe. From the law of gravitation, and using the general laws of motion, Newton was able to deduce Kepler's laws. The essence of his explanation can be expressed in popular terms by saying: If the inertia alone were acting (i.e. if there were no gravity) the planet would move on uniformly in a straight line, and thus would leave the neighbourhood of the sun. If gravity alone were acting (i.e. if the planet had no initial motion of its own) the planet would fall into the sun. The actual orbit is a compromise of the two effects of inertia and gravity; gravity binding the planet to the sun, inertia keeping it from falling into the sun. In addition to explaining Kepler's laws Newton was able to improve on them. Kepler's laws follow strictly if there is just the sun and one planet. But the gravitational influence of the other planets disturbs the orbit of a planet, and these disturbances Newton was able to predict according to the observations with every desired degree of precision.

It is completely justifiable that Newton's system, once it had come to be understood, impressed the public opinion of the coming centuries as the greatest work of natural science. Now for the first time natural science had achieved what was done in Greek mathematics: it had deduced statements which proved true in every detail, from a few clear and simple axioms. It is not surprising that an explanation of nature was considered for two centuries to be a reduction of observed phenomena to the principles discovered by Newton.

But, strictly speaking, Newton had not even achieved a complete reduction of the observed planetary motions to his own principles, and he knew it very well. Newton was on the line of Kepler. He was able to explain and to improve on Kepler's laws, a thing Descartes had been unable to do. But Newton, on the other hand, could offer no explanation of those facts that were explained satisfactorily by Descartes' eddy: the nearly circular shape of the orbits and their common orientation in space. As I said before, three things must be known to explain a particular motion, the third being the particular initial conditions. Mathematically this is due to the fact that Newton's laws imply differential equations with respect to time. The force only determines the change of the motion. Hence the motion in a later moment of time will depend on the motion in an earlier moment as well as on the force. A planetary orbit is fixed only when the position and velocity of the planet at some particular time is given.

Thus particular initial values and directions of the velocities of the individual planets had to be assumed in order to explain the high regularity of the system which had seemed so natural to Descartes. If, say, the original motion of one planet had been perpendicular to the plane in which the other planets move, it would have gone on moving in a plane perpendicular to the plane of the other planets. Similarly, had its initial velocity been too great, too small, or not directed in the tangent of a circle around the sun, the planet would have moved in a more or less eccentric ellipse or perhaps even in a parabola or a hyperbola. Newton could point to examples for these other cases: the comets are moving through the same space as the planets but all with odd eccentric elliptical and hyperbolical orbits oriented in all directions. This was even his most cogent argument against Descartes: how could there be such different motions of celestial bodies through the same space if the motion in this space was governed by one huge vortex of continuous matter? We can be certain that there is no continuous medium in the solar system that would exert any appreciable influence on the motions of planets and comets.

But then the regularity of the system remains unexplained. We can just say: God has been pleased to arrange the initial motions of the planets in such a way that they would follow these highly regular circular co-planar orbits. That is what Newton actually said. And Bentley in his sermons transformed this thought into a proof of the existence of God, the proof from the gaps of science. Science explains Kepler's laws, but it does not explain the initial conditions. But the initial conditions show a high regularity. Hence recourse must be had to the idea of an intelligent maker of the universe, of the *demiourgos*. It is true that Newton and Bentley considered the laws of nature to be ordained by God as well as the initial conditions. But the laws did not convince the sceptics of their divine origin; nature may just have laws of her own, depending on a God that made them. But where no laws of nature explain the order of nature, God must become manifest in his works even to the sceptic.

I said in the first lecture that in accepting this turn of the argument religion has already lost her case. I then pointed to the historical fact that the gaps of science are to be closed at some later date. We are to follow this development more closely. But now I should like to make use of the language I introduced in the lecture on Christianity. The concept of a nature obeying her own laws independent of the existence of God, seems to express precisely that post-Christian, secularized reality which I introduced there as a third element after nature and Christianity. Here equivocations must be avoided. The word nature then meant human nature as interpreted by Christianity, it meant the world of natural drives, of traditional institutions, of self-interpretation by myth. As I tried to point out when speaking of Galileo, the concept of exact mathematical laws of nature which was only dimly present in Greek thought gained far greater convincing power by means of the Christian concept of creation. Thus I think it is a gift of Christianity to the modern mind. Now we see how this inherited gift is used against the religion whence it came. And this killing of one's own parent by the weapon inherited from him becomes more and more naive. Kepler was a sincere Christian who adored God in the mathematical order of the world. Galileo, and even more Newton, being a more religious man, were sincere Christians who were interested in God's work. But while Galileo had still to defend his right to read God's greatness in the book of nature, Newton had to defend his idea of nature as a book written by God. Modern scientists in general find it very difficult to think of a religious interpretation of natural law as anything but an additional tenet, probably mythical and certainly not logically connected with the concept of laws of nature. No good will and no religious fervour can reverse this development. Modern secularized reality can in fact be interpreted in terms that take no account of religion at all. Science does not prove the existence of God. This should never be forgotten by those who want to understand the modern world in religious terms. On the other hand it will be good to see that the tree on which this now floating seed of modern science has grown was Christianity; that it was a sort of Christian radicalism which transformed nature from the house of gods into the realm of law.

I shall go ahead to Kant's cosmogony only by an intermediate step. The greatest contemporary and, in a sense, adversary of Newton was Leibniz; and in his philosophical outlook, the young Kant of the cosmogony follows the lines of Leibniz. The difference between Newton and Leibniz is probably most clearly seen in the letters exchanged between Leibniz and Samuel Clarke (who is there just Newton's spokesman) during the last years of Leibniz's life.

Leibniz there attacks Newton's concept of absolute space. This concept has a long pre-history of its own. As I said in the fourth lecture, Greek philosophy and mathematics had no concept of an independent entity like Newton's space. Plato's *chora* is more like a matter than like space, the atomists' *kenon* is somehow the non-existent, and Aristotle defines the *topos*, the place of a body, relative to the surrounding bodies, thus consciously avoiding the puzzling problem of a non-corporeal space. In a finite world every motion can be referred to the frame of the world itself. The idea of an infinite world made the question urgent: are position and motion only relative concepts, describing relations between bodies, or is there such a thing as absolute position and absolute motion? If this question is not answered, the law of inertia is meaningless, for how are we to know what we mean by uniform motion in a straight line if we do not know what is the frame of reference? Newton answered the question by his idea that there is an absolute space and an absolute time, which define absolute motion and hence the meaning of inertial motion. Under the aspects of physics I shall return to this idea and its criticism as given by Mach and Einstein, in the second series of lectures.

Leibniz opposed absolute space for philosophical reasons. What is the difference (thus we may briefly express his argument) between our actual world and a world that would result from it by transplanting everything ten miles without changing any relative positions; or between this world and a world which God would have created an hour earlier without changing any temporal relations? The two worlds cannot be distinguished. Hence, Leibniz says with an argument that might appeal to modern positivists, the two worlds are the same world. This means that absolute space and absolute time are nonsense. Now Leibniz' principle of the identity of indiscernibles does not apply to cases where we are just unable to distinguish two things practically. He only says that things are identical which have exactly identical attributes. This, he maintains, however, is just the case of the two worlds. Clarke replies that since Sir Isaac Newton has proved the existence of absolute space the two worlds do have different attributes: their different positions in absolute space, and their different initial moments in absolute time. Leibniz retorts that God would not have had a sufficient reason to create the world rather here than there, and rather now than then, and that hence the principle of sufficient reason would have been violated in the creation if Newton were right. Clarke says that there is a sufficient reason for God's having created the world here rather than there: God's will. Leibniz thinks that Clarke has too low a notion of God, thinking that God, like man, can act wilfully; God's will is always guided by God's reason. Clarke on his side thinks that Leibniz has too low a notion of God, thinking that his own human reason can fathom the depth of God's reasons for his decisions. Leibniz died before his final reply.

Leibniz here argues along the lines of his theodicy. God had the choice between an infinite number of possible worlds. He created this world because it was the best of all possible worlds. This was the sufficient reason for his choice. It is the best world because of its order, and in principle everything in it must be understandable out of its optimality. Mathematical laws express this order on a certain level of universality; the structure of the planetary system expresses it in a great particular example, but the same considerations must be able, in principle, to explain both. This is the philosophical background to the earlier years of Kant.

What Kant tried in his cosmogonical theory was in fact to unite the virtues of Descartes' cosmology with those of the science founded by Newton. Newton had proved that there was no vortex of continuous matter in the planetary system as we see it. Descartes, however, demonstrated that the motions of the planets show a regularity which might be explained by assuming such a vortex. Newton was unable to explain this regularity and said that God made the system like that long ago. This is not to be denied, but perhaps we can find out how God then made the system. Perhaps he made use of the Cartesian eddy? Kant does not expose his problem exactly in these words, but I think this is what he really achieves. In the beginning of the solar system there was, according to Kant, a large rotating nebula. Gravity made its main bulk condense in the centre, giving rise to the sun, and made parts of it condense in the outer regions, where they became the planets with their satellites. As to the origin of the first cloud Kant had ideas similar to those of the atomists and of Descartes, only he now applied Newton's laws consistently. He understood correctly that the galaxy was a large disk, a system of stars to which the sun belongs, and he explained its development by applying the same argument on a higher level. He rightly interpreted some elliptical nebulae—we know today that most of them have a spiral structure—as being similar systems outside our own galaxy. He ended by speculations on evolution passing in infinite time through infinite spaces, and on possible inhabitants of other planets and their moral values, thereby charmingly fitting in with the 18th century frame of mind.

Mathematically Kant's work is not more elaborate than that of Descartes. Forty years later Laplace proposed a similar theory in a simple and concise form, but still without attempting calculations about it which would, indeed, have been very difficult. Only then was Kant's theory brought out of oblivion, and through the 19th century the theory of Kant and Laplace was considered to be the mechanical explanation of the origin of the world. Then for the first time the methods of science had advanced so far that a quantitative treatment of the problem could be tried. I shall say a few words in the ninth lecture about the varying views on the theory to which these calculations led. I may say now that astrophysicists of our days have come to think that Kant was right in principle.

Kant's theology, as expressed in the preface of his book, is still more or less Leibnizian. Of course, in contrast to Leibniz, he now accepts Newton's mechanics without any qualifications. But he thinks that God made the world by using his own laws of nature. The view that "blind necessity" can have produced the order we see in the system is repugnant to him. Theologically he can argue that the necessity of a law installed by God is not blind; the material agent may not know where it is led by necessity, but God knew where it would be led. Historically it may be added that the concept of blind necessity has its origin in a non-mathematical theory of nature, or, in Plato, is opposed to mathematics, while the natural laws of science are just mathematical laws, corresponding to reason. I think he is right in thinking that he argues according to the Christian idea of creation.

Yet in Kant's own life this was not to be the final standpoint. In his later philosophy the mathematical structure which we find in science is no longer ascribed to God's creation but to the *a priori* forms of intuition and categories of the perceiving and knowing mind. Reason itself prescribes the laws to nature. We no longer understand the order of God's work because we are made in his image, but we understand the order of the phenomena because the phenomena of our experience have only become possible by the structure of the mind which experiences them. There is no longer a theoretical proof for the existence of God, neither in metaphysics, and neither by the gaps nor by the successes of sciences; the gaps are to be closed, and to explain the successes is the task of the *Critique of Pure Reason*. In this sense secularization has now reached the light of reason itself. Kant did not therefore cease to ask for God; on the contrary, this question can be understood to have been the impelling force behind all of his philosophy. Yet the weight of the question is transferred to the field of morality. In theoretical metaphysics the idea of God is now of regulative use only, and as such it influences science no longer in physics, but still in biology. According to the *Critique of Judgment* we can never hope to explain by physics the wonderful aspects of purpose in living organisms, and hence we must treat them, methodically, as though they were works of a purposeful divine reason. Thus Kant takes up the theme to which I shall devote the following lecture.

However, Kant was concerned till the end of his life with the explanation of the special laws of nature such as those which he used when in his youth he explained the origin of the planets. I think, it cannot be said that he solved this problem. I shall revert to Kant's theory of experience in the second lecture-series. Here I had to mention it in order to show that the youthful Kant's vindication of the Christian concept of creation against the inverted Platonism in Bentley's argument was in itself ambiguous. In fact, Kant's theory is a further step of secularization, whatever its author wanted it to be.

8 The Evolution of Life

WE have been speaking of the origin of heaven and earth, or, to put it in modern words, of the sun and its planets. But remember what I said about the Old Testament. Heaven and earth are only the stage. Grass and fruit are needed for the scenery, fish and fowl, beasts and cattle for 'extras', and the drama to be played is the history of man. God made every one of them after his kind. Science that had set out to explain the origin of earth and stars according to the laws of nature had to face the question how life on earth has come about.

I have never studied the history of biology in any detail. Hence I shall concentrate on the problems of principle which come to the forefront whenever the questions in these lectures are discussed with intelligent biologists of our time.

The problem of the evolution of life can be divided into three or four subquestions:

1. Has there been an evolution at all?

2. Can we give a causal explanation of evolution?
3. Do plants and animals form a separate realm of nature or does evolution bridge the gaps
   a. between inorganic matter and organic life?
   b. between brute animals and man?

These questions form a series of increasing importance for our problem of the relation between religious and scientific thought. Speaking of earlier times, I have tried to speak their language up to the point where I may have become obscure to a modern mind; but I did not see how we could hope to understand the questions inherited from those times without understanding their frame of mind. This is an excuse, addressed to the modern scientist. Now I have to make a similar excuse to the religious person. Speaking of modern science we shall have to face its ways of thought as clearly as possible. If you do not see what the scientific mind can achieve you will not understand our century. I have tried to speak like an ancient Jew and like a Platonic philosopher; I shall now speak like an ultra-scientist. And, strangely enough, in all three cases I do not need to say many things which I do not believe.

The first question: has there been an evolution at all? was settled in the 19th century by a bluntly positive answer. The steps of the ladder leading to this insight are simple enough. The first step is classification. As I said in the third lecture, already Genesis 1 shows a marked classificatory interest; in this respect the first chapter of the Bible is early science rather than myth. Greek biology, of which, for example, the wonderfully detailed studies of Aristotle are preserved, did a great deal of careful work. How, then, did these many species arise? Have they been in existence since infinite time, as Aristotle thought? Did God make them all in the first week, each after his kind? In the 18th century documents on earlier forms of life on earth became well known, and the idea that the earth has slowly formed entered into the scientific mind, progressing from astronomy to geology and biology. Early in the 19th century Cuvier still thought that there were sequences of geological catastrophes, each of which was followed by a direct creation of new types of living beings. This view is a biological analogy to Newton's and Bentley's view of the planetary system. It could not be upheld against the increasing amount of evidence for a more or less continuous transformation of organic forms. Most of the credit for this idea is probably to be given to Lamarck; Darwin's and Huxley's spectacular public success was in this question only indicating that the general public had become aware of the problem. Today, evolution as such is no longer questioned by serious biologists. And religious thought has found it easy to acquiesce along the lines I indicated when speaking of Kant: why should God have refrained from using the natural laws of growth and transformation in creating living beings?

But once the fact of evolution is admitted, the question of its causal explanation cannot be evaded. We are accustomed to plants and animals descending from parents similar to themselves. We are accustomed—that means that we cannot explain this fact either. But the question of the causality of events becomes more outstanding when events become known with which we are not acquainted; the well-known is the thing whose mysterious nature we realize last. From the modern point of view, however, we have to combine both questions: how is ordinary heredity to be explained and how the apparently even higher achievement of life, its upward evolution?

Here I first want to discuss a question of principle. Earlier views on organic life which have not completely disappeared even today would have led to a negative answer to the very attempt to ask such a question. One would have said: Life cannot be explained mechanically. Life is an entity of its own nature. It is not to be understood by concepts of causality but by concepts of finality. You will never be able to explain how an eagle's eye, a dog's nose, a lion's tooth have come about. But you can easily see what they are for: the eye is there for seeing, the nose for scenting, the tooth for biting. Explanation in the realm of life can only mean to tell us the what for, not the whence. This view seems to be favoured by the great authority of Aristotle, and it very naturally leaves the gap for religion: living beings are as they are because God made them such.

This view, I think, is wrong. But we shall learn a good deal by trying to say precisely in what respect it is wrong. For the flatly opposite view held by the popular philosophy of many modern biologists is, as I am afraid, no less wrong.

What is wrong in this view is not that it uses final concepts at all but that it opposes them to causal explanation. In this it is only in a very limited way warranted by Aristotle's own views which, as usual, are closer to common sense than anything believed by later thinkers. Let me make a few remarks on his famous four causes. This excursion may seem to lose time, but in fact it may gain time for the modern problems by clarifying some concepts in advance.

Aristotle applies four concepts to every existing thing which he himself calls its four *archai*, its four beginnings or origins. In Latin they are called the four causes: *causa materialis*, *formalis*, *efficiens*, and *finalis*. As examples, look at this glass and at this apple-seed. Both have a *causa materialis*, the matter they are made from or consist of: the glass tumbler consists of the particular mixture of silicate we call glass, the apple-seed consists of a complicated mixture of organic compounds. Both have a formal cause, a form. Here remember what idea or form meant in Plato's philosophy; it is the answer to the question: what is this thing? Thus the form can to some extent be identified with the species; the word species in fact translates the Greek *eidos* or *idea* into Latin. The form of the glass tumbler is that it is a glass tumbler; if you want a definition I say it is a cup-like thing in which liquid can be contained for drinking. The form of the apple-seed is that it is an apple-seed; you will permit me not to bother you with a verbal definition of an apple-seed.

If you think that these two *archai* or causes are highly trivial you are perhaps right. Aristotle wanted to formulate the simplest statements which can be made saying what a given thing is, and simple statements tend to sound trivial. Philosophy on the extremely high level of methodical self-control on which Aristotle is thinking begins by trying to be aware of what we really say in our apparently trivial everyday speech. Thus everything admits of at least two questions: what is it?—the answer is its form, its species, and: what does it consist of or what is it made of?—the answer is its matter. Matter in the Aristotelian sense thus is not an ultimate substance, but a concept of relation: the matter of the glass tumbler, the chemical substance glass, has a form and a matter of its own: to the chemist, for example, its form would be indicated by its chemical formula and its matter might be the atoms of silicon, oxygen and other elements. The atoms in their turn have a form described by atomic physics and a matter called elementary particles. What about the elementary particles? Let us wait for the second series of lectures.

Now most things admit of two further questions: how has this thing been made or come into being? and what was it made for? This glass tumbler was perhaps made by a glass-blower; in this case the glass-blower is its *causa efficiens*. The apple-seed was not made by human design. It grew on an apple-tree. The apple-tree is its *causa efficiens*. This glass tumbler was made for your Gifford lecturer to quench his thirst. This is its *causa finalis*. This apple-seed grew in order that there should be a chance of another apple-tree growing out of it. This is its *causa finalis*.

Here we reach the critical point. The modern biologist is tempted to say: now Aristotle in the end has turned out to be the metaphysician we always suspected him to be. The apple-seed has not grown for any purpose; it just grew according to the laws of nature. But this criticism is only half correct. I admit that even Aristotle could not quite avoid metaphysics. He could not explain the things we see quite without assumptions about entities which we do not see. Just as the modern scientist believes in such things as laws of nature which nobody has ever seen and which cannot even ever be proved strictly, Aristotle believes in some ultimate finality in the world. But as we can offer many examples in which the visible events follow very closely the laws which we have stated hypothetically, Aristotle can offer many examples in which things behave very precisely according to his hypothetical ultimate finality. Our simple examples are in the fields of physics and astronomy, his are in the field of biology. If there were no apple-seeds, apple-trees would soon disappear from the world; if eagles had no eyes, dogs no noses, lions no teeth, they would be unable to survive. If you use the final concepts only as a description of the actual functioning of all these organs you stay within a simple phenomenology of organic life. Modern biologists avoid the word finality because they do not want to imply the metaphysical hypothesis of conscious design, and they are certainly right in that. But in words like "function" or "use" of an organ they describe exactly the phenomena to which Aristotle's concept of *causa finalis* pointed.

Thus, if we could stay within the framework of pure phenomenology there would be no conflict between causal and final explanation. According to Aristotle we do not have to choose between causal and final explanations. On the contrary, every thing that has a final cause, an end for which it is made, also has a *causa efficiens*, for it cannot have sprung out of nothing. Just because lecturers want to drink water, a glass-blower was needed to make the glass. Since the eagle needs an eye there arises the task for the physiologist to understand how this necessary organ could grow in the embryo in the egg according to the laws of chemistry. This is very mysterious but it must have happened somehow. The idea that the laws of physics and chemistry should have been violated in this process of growth is, I think, not of the slightest use for a better understanding of the usefulness of the eye to the eagle. Leibniz pointed out that a clock fulfils its maker's design not by disobeying the laws of mechanics but on the contrary only because these laws are followed strictly by its springs and wheels.

Yet, by tacitly introducing the modern concept of strict laws of nature instead of Aristotle's *causa efficiens*, I have disturbed the balance between causality and finality. Aristotle's *causa efficiens* is guided by the potentiality of the end for which the thing is produced. The glass-blower knows that tumblers are needed and makes them for that purpose. The apple-tree, not having a rational soul, subjectively knows nothing of its objective ends, but Aristotle needed the concept of the *dynamis*, the *potentia*, i.e. what a thing by its own nature is destined to become, if he wanted to describe the facts of organic life. But if every event in this world is determined unambiguously from the preceding state by strict laws of nature, no space is left for additional determinations by design or by any other principle. This is a difference not always realized by philosophers who try to harmonize finalism with physics: civil laws determine only part of the actions of men, thus leaving space for other agencies; laws of physics, as modern times have come to understand them, are sufficient to determine the events, given the initial state. Civil laws can be supplemented; laws of physics, if not leading by themselves to the result we see, must have been broken. Whether quantum-mechanical indeterminacy will change much on this point I am inclined to doubt. Thus modern science seems to put before us this alternative: either biological finality is nothing but another expression of what follows from physical law; or the laws of physics do not hold in living organisms, at least not without exceptions.

Here we encounter a situation exactly similar to that left to Kant by Newton. As long as physics and chemistry offered no established hope of ever being able to explain the wonderful teleology of living organisms, there was a gap in science that clearly seemed to point to direct divine creation. Now the degree of complication in organisms is far higher than in the planetary systems. While the system of the planets is certainly beautiful and fairly well-ordered, it contains no element that calls for comparisons to works of human instrumental design or to that design itself like the organs and instincts of living beings. It was Darwin's ingenious idea that chance and natural selection in the struggle for survival might explain the apparent finality in life. He introduced a truly historical way of thought into the science that is concerned with the history of nature. We should not be surprised, he says, to find only forms of life that are fit for survival; if they had not been fit they would not have survived.

Of course Darwin could not strictly prove his theory. Such a proof does not exist up to this day, and it may be doubted how it could be given except negatively, by excluding all other possibilities. First of all, it is always difficult to prove theories about past events that cannot be repeated experimentally. Even Kant's theory of the planets cannot today, after two hundred years of astronomical discoveries, be considered as finally settled, in any case in its details (see following lecture). Even a convincing argument showing that Darwin's theory might possibly be correct is not quite easily given, if we consider the quantitative aspect. Can chance supply a sufficient number of steps towards higher organisation within the available age of the earth which we now consider to be about four or five thousand million years? There are still biologists who flatly deny that this can be possible, while others—I think the majority—feel it might very well have happened in the way proposed by Darwin, taking account of the more modern concept of mutations.

I am not going to discuss this calculus of probabilities. I only want to point out what kind of arguments may enter the discussion by giving one example that always strikes me for its existential meaning to our human pursuit of happiness. Most organs and properties of living beings serve to keep the individual alive, like everything connected with eating, self-defence, etc. There are others that preserve the existence of the species, like the organs and instincts of sexuality and those by which the offspring are protected. But I think that there are also properties which serve to promote evolution. A species which—by chance, as Darwin thinks—may have acquired a property which makes this species develop faster than others towards different forms, will thereby have an advantage in the struggle for survival; thus properties of this kind will tend to survive themselves and perhaps become common. Now I feel that one of these properties is mortality, or, to speak more strictly, shortlivedness. The more generations a species produces per unit time the more different mutations or combinations of mutations will have a chance of being tried out. There is a strong selection pressure—to use this technical term of selection theory—favouring a good protection of the lives of young individuals; thus the love of parents for their children is common among higher animals. There is, however, no selection pressure favouring the survival of old individuals once they have generated and protected a sufficient number of children. On the contrary, they now become useless eaters. Thus love of adult children for their parents is very rarely seen in animals; the far wider and deeper vision of man seems to be needed in order to understand that caring for the old is a meaningful task. In plant and animal life, a short remaining life-span of the old ones is favourable for the species. Perhaps the natural process of ageing would never have developed without this selection pressure, for I see no biochemical reason why individuals should not be possible that would stay alive indefinitely if not killed by force, just as a species can stay in existence for a million or even a hundred million years.

For our further consideration I shall treat Darwin's theory as if it were true—not because of a positive proof but because I have never heard a positive argument for its impossibility that looked convincing to me. I thus use Occam's razor: why look for additional causes of evolution as long as we do not know that those given by Darwin are not sufficient? As I pointed out when speaking of Copernicus and the Greeks, Occam's razor can be a very misleading instrument. We should never use it dogmatically. Here I only use it to simplify the language when I try to explain what could be the consequences of taking modern scientific biology as seriously as it deserves. If a theory different from Darwin's, but still lying within the conceptual framework of modern science, should be found, probably not much would be changed in my further arguments.

I come to the third question which is twofold in itself: the question about the possible limitations of evolutionary theory at the lower and upper end of plant and animal life. Has life developed out of inorganic matter? Has man developed out of higher animals, say apes?

I think the answer to both questions as given by modern biologists is: with high probability yes. The natural production of amino-acids under conditions similar to those that may have prevailed on the earth long ago, has been proved in the laboratory. How proteins may have formed out of these amino-acids, and how living beings may have formed out of or together with the proteins is not well understood, but who can deny the possibility? And how else should life have begun after the earth had been formed from gas and dust?

Similarly we speak about man. Geological evidence shows that man is a newcomer on the earth. Discussion may be possible whether he is one or ten million years old; if the complete age of the earth were compressed into the twenty-four hours of a day this means discussing whether man arrived half a minute or five minutes before midnight. Whence should he have sprung if not from the higher animals? Perhaps the ape may still be doubtful as an ancestor. Not long ago I read in a newspaper that new results had made it probable that man did not descend from the ape; looking more closely into the matter the new theory turned out to maintain that he descended from the half-ape.

Perhaps more remarkable than these views of modern science is the way of arguing which I could use in order to make them plausible. Where else than in inorganic matter should life have its origin; where else than in animals should man find his ancestors? We see no other possible origin. But neither did earlier generations see another origin. Their conclusion was, however, different from ours; they looked for an origin in the sphere of things invisible. It is not by its conclusions but by its methodical starting point that modern science excludes direct creation. Our methodology would not be honest if it denied this fact. We do not possess positive proof of the inorganic origin of life or of the primate ancestry of man, perhaps not even for evolution itself if we want to be pedantic. But I confess that I would consider it quite useless to deduce any scepticism with respect to evolutionary views from this argument. Science has been successful in this kind of generalisation so many times that I would be afraid of repeating Bellarmine's and Bentley's mistakes if I were to doubt this most natural hypothesis on the one evolutionary track leading from the atom to man. I am to ask quite a different question: do we know what we mean by such a hypothesis? Strangely enough it is easier to formulate and even to prove scientific views than to say in clear concepts what we mean by the words we use in such a formulation. The second series of these lectures will be full of this kind of analysis of meaning *a posteriori*.

If life grew out of inorganic matter, and if natural selection suffices as an explanation of evolution, it is a very natural additional assumption that the known laws of physics and chemistry hold within organic bodies without any exception. This assumption is by no means necessary. For example, there might be laws of forces producing only extremely small effects in single atoms but producing decisive effects in large bodies that are organized like living cells and organisms. Under the impression of the difficulty of explaining the phenomena of life by physics and chemistry some of the leading physicists of our time, like Bohr, Heisenberg, Pauli, have explicitly rejected this explanation. Yet I do not want to follow them, again in order to simplify the argument in a still undecided case; for the time being I shall cut out their very interesting views from my trend of thought by means of Occam's razor.

Thus I seem to assume that any living being, including man, is nothing but a piece of physico-chemical machinery. In fact I want to withstand the impact of this view not by escaping into any more or less metaphysical hypothesis but by sheer analysis of its meaning.

Give me credit for accepting the view. If you do so, I conclude: We, living conscious human beings, assembled in this lecture hall in Glasgow University, have come to the conclusion that we are nothing but physical engines. What is it I have said in saying this? Let me take the statement word by word.

"Nothing but" is a beautiful phrase. I am speaking to you. What is speech? Well, nothing but sound waves. But these sound waves carry a meaning—at least I hope they do. What do we mean by "meaning"? This is easily understood and difficult to define. It is not for the sound waves you have come here but for their meaning. But does this imply that the laws of acoustics would have to break down somewhere in order that the sound should be able to carry a meaning? I should say, on the contrary.

Go on and ask what it is in the sound waves that carries the meaning. It is certainly somehow inherent in their particular structure. Theories of information try to measure their content of information in an objective manner. I shall not go into its details; in any case it must be an audible feature of the sound waves, some element of form in them, that carries the meaning.

But probably you will say that the meaning is present only in conscious minds. There must be somebody to listen; I would not preach to the bare walls. How, then, does the meaning-bearing structure of the sound waves enter into your minds? We can follow this process by three or four steps. The sound waves make the tympanum vibrate. This mechanical vibration excites the nerve of the ear to carry a chemico-electrical signal towards the brain. There the signal is somehow brought into contact with many other signals in a way not at all well known to science. Finally your body shows some reaction: concentrated looks at the lecturer, writing down of notes, perhaps sleeping. Where is the mind in this description?

I described what I could see or infer from my scientific knowledge. But to every person in this room there is one person who experiences the process quite differently: this is the person himself or herself. And I should add, others do so, too, in fact. You do not just look at my physical behaviour; you would not be here for this purpose. Listening to my words you know a bit about what is in my mind. Looking at you I know a bit—a bit less probably—of what is in your minds. Mind is known to mind, however this may happen.

I gave you a description; I shall not transform it into a metaphysical hypothesis. The problem of matter and mind, like many other things I have mentioned so far, belongs to the second lecture series. Here I just stay with my original question, asking whether this problem would seem to become in any way more understandable by the assumption that the laws of physics did not hold strictly in our brains? I see no reason why this should be so. Thus to say that we are nothing but physical engines still seems to be a sentence devoid of a clear meaning; but that under the aspects of physics we can be described as physical engines is a statement that might make sense.

Then we take the next step in our analysis. What do we mean by "physical engine". Take a motor-car as an example. Are we such things as motor-cars?

One difference is evident. Machines are built by man according to a plan in order to fulfil a limited purpose. Man is not built by man. Life—as Bohr sometimes says—is not an experiment of ours. Man has a history of his own. Machines belong to the history of man.

But how relevant is this difference? Does it mean that the really important traits of living beings will never be imitated by man-built machines? We here enter the field of research called cybernetics.

A motor-car is not to be compared to a living being but to one of its organs, say to its feet. Human beings are born of human beings, cars are not born of cars; but neither are feet born of feet. The car imitates one particular activity of animals: locomotion. Radar imitates another one: vision. Calculating machines probably offer the most relevant comparison; they imitate certain activities of the mind. Man is not in practice interested in a machine that imitates all of his actions at once, but in machines which do better than man himself in a very limited field.

Thus, take the most relevant example, the imitation of the mind by electronic calculators. As I said in the first lecture, their degree of complexity so far is comparable to the nervous system of an earth worm; hence we will not expect them to imitate man very well. Still they have beaten him definitely in numerical calculations and I have studied myself the first game of draughts played by an electronic calculator. The machine was still inferior to its inventor in this game. But probably machines will improve faster than the human brain. Where are the limits?

A machine cannot make another machine, you will say. This is not so certain. Certainly a very simple machine cannot build another one. At a higher level of complexity this may change. J. von Neumann has outlined a machine that would be able to compile one exactly equal to itself out of some simple "bricks". One may think of a machine which would have to be even more complicated and which would be able to build another one superior to itself. Where are the limits?

A machine does not act spontaneously, you will say. This is not so certain. I am told by a man who knows the facts that when the draught-playing machine was about to lose its first game, it cheated. Whenever I tell this story to laymen in the presence of calculator-specialists, the specialist is eager to explain: "but that, of course, was only a mistake". Of course it was a mistake, it was so by definition. Whenever the machine does what we have not planned it to do we call it a mistake. But even if we rule out such mistakes which are contrary to the programme, we have to admit that we do not know in advance what will come out when the machine obeys the programme; else we would not have cared to build the machine. For the simple programmes of existing machines at least some general expectations about the results can be given. But in any case a machine is a real thing and what it can do once it is built need not be identical with what we think it can do. Where are the limits?

A machine does not have consciousness, you say. How do you know that? I admit the statement, but I admit it since comparison with animals and with the human brain makes it appear improbable that the precise activities of existing machines have any close similarity to activities of nervous systems which are connected with what we call consciousness. But as long as you have not solved the problem of the mutual relationship of matter and consciousness, how can you know that machines cannot have consciousness?

It is an ancient human dream to make a human being. I do not see that our present knowledge proves that this is impossible. Probably, if we could build a man, it would be a horrible thing really to do it. It might be the final sacrilege and its consequences might be disastrous. Perhaps we are rightly afraid of it, and perhaps our fear takes the form of the belief that it is impossible. I think many of our beliefs are disguised fears. In fact, again, I think it will not be possible. But the reason might just be that what you need to make a man is history; perhaps it cannot be done in less than four thousand million years.

You should rightly understand this repeated question: where are the limits? I want to say how little we know about these questions, and how impossible it is even to make negative statements. In order to understand the problem better we would first have to go on with our analysis of meaning. I said that under the aspects of physics we might be likened to physical engines. What are the aspects of physics? Do we know what we mean by the laws of physics that are supposed to hold in our body? As to this question, however, I once again refer to the second series of lectures. It will be their guiding question.

9 *Modern Astronomy*

IN this lecture I shall try briefly to describe the actual status of the cosmogonical problem, beginning with factual aspects, and ending with the philosophical questions.

Let us start from the biological theories as outlined in the preceding lecture. We do not yet understand the causes of evolution too well, but we have very little doubt about the fact of evolution; it is even most commonly held that organic life has developed out of what we call inorganic matter in the early stages of geological history. What are the reasons for this general belief? In the last lecture I formulated them negatively: We do not know how life should have come to exist in its actual form in any other way. This formulation leaves silently aside any possible supernatural origin of life; such is the faith in science of our time which we all share. But in order to be convincing our belief in evolution must at least be founded on an analysis of possible alternatives that lie within the frame of natural law.

We believe that living beings can only descend from living beings rather similar to themselves. If, say, monkeys or oak trees did not descend from mammals or trees on our earth they might only descend from mammals or trees outside our earth. It seems that flying saucers do not yet belong to the trusted elements of the scientific faith; in any case they have not led to any scientific theory of an extraterrestrial origin of higher forms of terrestrial life. The theory, however, was put forward more than fifty years ago, that at least the most primitive forms of life might be able to resist the physical conditions of cosmic space, and that in this way life might wander from star to star and might thus be as eternal as the universe was then thought to be. Today this theory seems less attractive, for two reasons. First, no evidence of life has been found so far in meteorites or in any ingredients of our atmosphere that might have a chance of being of cosmic origin. Secondly, the prevailing view of astronomers in our times is that not only the earth but probably the universe as a whole is not eternal but has had a beginning. This view is the main topic of my present lecture.

The age of the earth can be estimated to be of the order of magnitude of four thousand million years, plus or minus one thousand million years, perhaps. How can we give such an estimate?

For the details of this problem I may perhaps refer you to my lectures on the History of Nature. Here I shall only draw the main line of the argument.

Radio-active atoms decay at a fixed rate. Of a given amount of say, polonium, one half will be transformed into lead within 137 days; the corresponding time, the so-called half-life, is a little less than 2000 years for radium and about five thousand million years for uranium. Now there are typical minerals of uranium in the crust of the earth that contain an amount of lead which is greater in proportion to the age of the geological stratum in which they are found. This serves as a kind of clock which was set when the mineral was formed, and which gives us its actual age. Even the age of terrestrial rocks in general can be estimated in a similar way, using its average content of uranium and of lead isotopes. Indeed, the earth cannot be much older than the half-life of uranium, considering that there is still much uranium present on the earth and that no way is known in which uranium might have originated on the earth once the earth was existing as a planetary body.

Of course, this line of argument presupposes that the known laws of nature have held quite accurately all through the time that is to be measured by the uranium clock. Can we be certain that the decay rate of uranium has stayed constant through geological history? Our present answer is: this is by no means *a priori* certain, but it seems highly probable, considering that many different methods of estimating cosmic ages converge towards the same result. Again, I leave out the details. The point of principle is that we consider laws of nature as subjected to empirical proof which in many cases—as e.g. if we are interested in the far past of the universe—cannot be given by actual experimenting, but by accumulating the probability of a system of hypotheses. The hypotheses may lead to an ever increasing number of consistent predictions and interpretations of such facts as must be considered to be documents of the far past; and this is all we can hope for.

If the earth has a finite age it must have originated somehow, and in the ideas about the way in which it originated, modern astronomy, after some vacillations, has returned to views very similar to those proposed by Kant. Again, I leave the details aside. In any case, it seems probable today that the planets have formed out of a nebula that surrounded the sun. One of the most active investigators of our days, G. Kuiper at Yerkes Observatory, thinks that some denser parts of the nebula condensed further under the influence of their own gravity; this is precisely what Kant thought. I have proposed a slightly different theory in which the planetary bodies were formed out of dust that originated by chemical condensation of the heavier elements within the nebula. I do not know myself which theory I should prefer in our actual state of knowledge. In any case you see that the possible field of controversy is about points of the detailed mechanism but not on the principle.

But in our days such a theory is only a minor step in the ladder of cosmogonical questions. Whence did the nebula come? Part of which greater system is our planetary system? These questions to which Kant could only offer highly speculative answers are better understood today than the particular model of the origin of planets.

Let us first glance at the distribution of objects in space as we know or suppose them to exist now: the sun is quite an ordinary star, similar in its physical characteristics to the fixed stars which we see at night. One hundred thousand million (10^{11}) stars of this type, roughly speaking, form the system known as the galaxy, the bulk of which is not seen as individual stars but forms the cloudlike ring of the milky way. This system is something like a disk, not unlike a huge simile of what Kant considered to be the original shape of the planetary nebula. We are inside it, as we are inside the planetary system; thus the milky way, just like the zodiac, is a great circle on the sky. The similarity of shape implies a similarity of origin. The galaxy still contains large amounts of interstellar matter, in the state of gas or of dust, and it is natural to suppose that there was a time in which it consisted of an extended gas throughout. Then parts of it will have condensed into stars. An intermediate step of this condensation may have been the formation of the smaller, separate nebulae, one of which gave rise to our planetary system. We do not know positively whether other stars have planetary systems, too. But our actual knowledge contains no reason why at least some of them should not have planets. Thus astronomy has nothing to say against the speculations on life and on intelligent beings on other stars which are so popular today. Only the other planets of our own system seem less apt to carry higher forms of organic life than the earth, and thus the probability that intelligent beings from other stars will visit us may not be overwhelmingly great. But I should not dare to make a definite prediction.

The part of space that can be penetrated by our existing telescopes contains about a hundred million systems similar to our galaxy. In general they are termed spiral nebulae because many of them, our galaxy included, have a spiral structure. I shall not go into any detailed description of these systems. But I must spend a little time with the question of what lies beyond them.

It is not the unknown answer to this question but its methodological structure that should concern us here. The question is of a puzzling character. Of course we do not know what is beyond the limits of our knowledge; this is the definition of the word limit. Still we are convinced that there is something beyond these limits. How can we be convinced; do we have knowledge beyond our knowledge? In any case, we should say, there must be space outside the part of space we know. But how do we know that? Do we have an *a priori* knowledge of cosmic space, five thousand million light years from here? In our century Einstein has surprised the scientific world by assuming that perhaps our *a priori* assumptions on space are wrong. He offered the hypothesis that space itself has a mathematical property which can be imprecisely visualized by calling space itself curved. In a curved space a body flying along a straight line may return to its starting point. I think Einstein's particular assumption on cosmic space is neither proved nor disproved up to this day; in any case we know no reason why we should not consider it to be a theory as plausible as any that has been proposed. Now, if it is true, the question: what is beyond the limits of our knowledge? may sooner or later turn out to have a surprising answer. Beyond a certain limit there may neither be other galaxies nor will there be empty space but there might be the very same galaxies as on this side of the limit. If I may slightly simplify the historical facts, the history of geography may serve as an example. After Marco Polo's travels to China and after the discovery of America the Pacific was the limit of our geographical knowledge in the East and in the West, and when Magellan crossed it he found the same continents on both sides of the border.

The philosophical view about the nature of space that lies behind Einstein's hypothesis, is again a topic for my second lecture series. I had to mention it here for two reasons. Materially seen, it belongs to my intermediate subject matter, the distribution of objects in cosmic space; a subject matter I am leaving at this point where it ends, as usual, in an unproved hypothesis. Formally seen, Einstein's proposal shows what unexpected answers may be given to age-old questions. This we should keep in our minds when we now turn to our main topic which is not cosmic space but cosmic time.

I gave an estimate of the age of the earth. How old is the sun? How old are stars in general? How old is our galaxy? How old are galaxies in general? Is there anything like a well-defined age of the universe?

There has been a very marked convergence of empirical facts towards a universal statement which I shall express in two forms, one cautious and one less cautious. Being cautious we are entitled to say: There is good evidence for the assumption that there is a common time-scale of the evolution of most cosmic objects with a characteristic time-constant of roughly five thousand million (5.10^9) years.[1] Less cautiously we may yield to the temptation of saying: The universe has a finite age of $x.10^9$ years.

Again, referring you to more explicit presentations elsewhere, I shall mention the empirical evidence very briefly.

The sun is radiating away energy at a high rate. Today we are convinced that we know the sources of this radiation; it is the consequence of nuclear processes in the deep interior of the sun, processes not quite unlike those that take place in the hydrogen bomb. In fact, astrophysical theories on nuclear processes in the sun may have contributed to the idea of making a hydrogen bomb. Now the amount of hydrogen present in the sun is finite, and hence the sun cannot uphold its radiation indefinitely. Since the sun is still radiating it must have begun to radiate a certain time ago. This beginning, according to our present knowledge, may well have been $x.10^9$ years before the present era. The time span might also have been a little longer, but not much longer.

[1] Since these lectures were given, recent results seem to have shown that our quantitative estimate of the time-scale has been inaccurate. Ten or fifteen thousand million years are probably a better guess. I express this uncertainty by speaking of $x.10$ years in the printed text. I think nothing in principle is changed by this readjustment of a scale.

Similar arguments apply to all stars which we can see today. Recently it has become fairly certain that stars are being formed out of interstellar gas even in our time; but most stars seem to have an age not too far different from that of the sun, and there is no positive evidence for any age greater than the highest estimate indicated by the "x".

The inner dynamics of a galaxy—which is a rotating bulk of stars and interstellar matter—is not yet too well understood. Still, it seems quite plausible that galaxies themselves should develop within a similar time-scale. The strongest argument for this view is what I might call the outer dynamics of galaxies, that is what we know about their relative motions. The famous red shift of their spectral lines is most naturally explained by the assumption that they are all receding from each other, not unlike the pieces of an exploding bomb-shell. If Einstein is right in considering cosmic space to be curved this implies that its curvature is a function of time, the total volume of space increasing with time; in this sense the term "expanding universe" is often used. But we do not need to express the natural interpretation of empirical facts in the terms of Einstein's hypothesis. If we consider space to be Euclidean we may just speak of an expanding motion of all known matter within space, and we will have described the same observations. It must be admitted, however, that the motion itself is not seen. What we see is a red shift of spectral lines. Physics, as we know it today, does not offer any other natural explanation of this red shift than the assumed expanding motion; but whoever does not like the theory of expansion seems, in the present state of our knowledge, free to invent new laws of physics that would explain the red shift in a manner he likes better.

There is, however, one additional argument for considering the expanding motion as real, and in my view this argument is very strong. If there is a real motion, it defines a time-scale. Assume the comparison with an exploding bomb-shell as correct: then, if you can measure the distances and the velocities of the fragments in a given moment, you can calculate at which moment of time the explosion took place. Now the distances of galaxies are roughly known, and the red shift, if interpreted as indicating a velocity, gives you the numerical value of this velocity: hence we can calculate the time of the first explosion. It turns out to be roughly $x.10^9$ years ago. Thus, in a completely independent way we have come back to the same age as in our earlier estimates. This result would be a very surprising accident if the red shift were not caused by a real motion. I think this argument has convinced most astrophysicists, and it is the real reason for the common use of the term "age of the universe".

Of course, admitting this time-scale as meaningful, we are still very far from having a consistent theory of what happened $x.10^9$ years ago. How broad a scale of possible interpretations is still left I may indicate by mentioning two extreme views, both of which have found defenders. The metaphysically most conservative hypothesis, if I may say so, is that of the so-called theory of continuous creation. It says: Our own galaxy may be $x.10^9$ years old, and in any case this age indicates a characteristic time-scale of cosmic events; but in the universe taken as a whole nothing of any importance at all happened $x.10^9$ years ago or at any other time; the universe has always looked exactly the same way it looks today. The apparently most radical hypothesis says on the contrary: Not only the whole universe began to exist $x.10^9$ years ago; even time itself did not exist earlier, for before the world there was no time. I want to discuss these two views in more detail.

The theory of continuous creation has acquired a good deal of fame, mainly due to the gifts of imagination and of popular presentation of my honoured colleague Fred Hoyle. It satisfies the desire which, I think, must be termed metaphysically conservative in the scientific situation of our century, to reconcile the new empirical data with the traditional view of modern science that the universe has no beginning and no end in time. This is achieved by assuming that at any time and in any place some matter is originating (or "created") out of nothing. This matter will at times condense into galaxies. Looked at from the matter originating in other parts of the universe, matter is created with an initial velocity such that in the course of time it will drift into the infinity of space, thereby vacating the place where it originated for new matter to be created *ex nihilo*. The so-called expansion of the universe is nothing but this continuous drifting-away of matter continuously replaced, and the idea of an infinite space, which is absolutely necessary in this view, serves to secure sufficient room for the newcomers. This process is considered to have taken place since infinite time and to go on for infinite time, and thus on the average the universe will never change.

This is a very clever theory indeed. I know of no particular empirical facts that would favour it more than its competitors, and personally I admit that I hesitate to admit it as true or even as very probable. But my reasons are reasons of methodological taste on which a discussion cannot be decided. My own conservatism lies in the field of method rather than of metaphysics. Thus I would not be much shocked by having to admit a finite duration of time while I like to trust empirically established laws of nature as long as possible, not because I think them to be better than other possibilities but because I do not easily trust our scientific imagination to hit upon the right idea on merely speculative arguments. Thus the law of conservation of matter which in modern physics is identical with the law of conservation of energy is, in my mind, closely connected with the general structure of our existing physics, and we do not know how much we shall have to change if we sacrifice it to the idea of a continuous creation *ex nihilo*. There are moments in the history of science in which such a sacrifice of empirically so far well-established traditional views is needed in order to take a great step forward towards a new and more comprehensive harmony between theories and facts. I want to be forced towards such a step, however, and I see no empirical reason which would force me here; for the idea of an infinite duration of time is certainly not an empirical one.

The other extreme does not now admit of any empirical proof either; it is only intended to show the possibilities for which we ought to be prepared. If we stay methodologically conservative and assume no new production of matter out of nothing, the matter now contained in the visible part of the universe must have existed $x.10^9$ years ago, but in a far smaller space. This state of affairs cannot be extrapolated into the past beyond the time at which our simple model of linear expansion would lead to the absurd consequence that all matter was united in one mathematical point. Several suggestions of what was in the beginning have been made. Some of them assume an infinite time before the expansion which we see now started, e.g. a nearly stationary condensed Einstein universe. Others give the world a more or less abrupt start. I think there are good reasons for thinking that there are no strictly periodic solutions of the cosmological problem. These reasons are connected with the second law of thermodynamics which I have discussed at length in my *History of Nature* to which I may refer those who are interested in the problem. Yet besides this kind of very general statement I think nothing can be said positively about these events milliards of years ago, in any case on the basis of our existing knowledge. The thing I wanted to point out by speaking of another extreme is that modern theoretical physicists certainly do not need to be less critical of their own concepts than St. Augustine was when he felt that the concept of a time that elapsed before there was a world might be a completely meaningless concept. A modern positivist would not argue differently.

To sum up: I do not know whether the world has had a beginning, but it may well have had one. If, however, it did have a beginning, then time may have had a beginning as well. How this beginning would have to be imagined I do not know; and here it may be good to remember Einstein's theory of space, only as an example of unforeseen possibilities.

The rest of this lecture is to be devoted to the repercussions of this scientific situation on our general topic of human views on cosmogony and creation. I should like to begin by telling you a very simple story which I experienced myself and which, if I remember rightly, first made me think of the questions on which I have now been speaking so long. In 1938 when I was a young theoretical physicist in Berlin, I gave a paper in the "Physikalische Kolloquium" of the university of Berlin on the transmutation of elements in the sun. I had then just devised a particular nuclear reaction chain that could serve as source of energy for the sun. It was the so-called carbon cycle which was found independently and worked out in detail far more precisely by Bethe in the same year; from our present point of view it is the right type of reaction but not the one that actually plays the main rôle in the sun. In any case I was quite proud of my discovery, and in order to show its plausibility I stressed the point that it gave the sun a possible age which would fit in very well with the age of the universe defined by the red shift which at that time was a rather recent idea. On this point, however, I met the violent opposition of the famous physico-chemist Walther Nernst who belonged to an older generation and who then held the chair of physics in the university. He said, the view that there might be an age of the universe was not science. At first I did not understand him. He explained that the infinite duration of time was a basic element of all scientific thought, and to deny this would mean to betray the very foundations of science. I was quite surprised by this idea and I ventured the objection that it was scientific to form hypotheses according to the hints given by experience, and that the idea of an age of the universe was such a hypothesis. He retorted that we could not form a scientific hypothesis which contradicted the very foundations of science. He was just angry, and thus the discussion, which was continued in his private study, could not lead to any result; Professor F. Debye in whose institute I was then working and who had accompanied us to Nernst's room finished it by the Salomonic remark: "Look, Herr Geheimrat. Dr. von Weizsäcker is interested in the particular problem of the energy sources of the sun, and you are interested in the problem of the universe as a whole; thus there is no contradiction between your views. Give him time. He is a young man, and if you are right, he will come to share your views in the end." Thus we still arrived home at the right time for dinner.

What impressed me about Nernst was not his arguments, in which I am afraid I still think there was no substance; what impressed me was his anger. Why was he angry? What vital interest of the man Walther Nernst who was born in the late 19th century and who was certain that he would die in the 20th, what vital interest of this man could possibly be violated by the possibility that the universe might not have existed since infinite time but that it might have come into existence five thousand million years ago? I realized that he was even more angry when I added that according to the second law of thermodynamics every finite part of the world had a finite number of possible states through which it could go just once and that, as our world was still changing today, it was very probable that it had not existed since an infinite time. He flatly denied this consequence of the second law. I have to admit that the application of the second law to the universe as a whole contains some intricate problems and cannot be done in a naive manner. But I easily saw that it was not this scientific difficulty which moved him but some kind of horror in face of the thought that this world might come to an end. The universe just *had* to be a thing to which concepts like age should not be applicable.

Reflecting on this attitude I wondered how a Platonist or a medieval Christian would react to the same scientific theories. The answer seemed clear. Neither the Platonist, believing in the immortality of the soul, nor the Christian, believing in a resurrection on a new earth, under a new heaven, would be troubled by the discovery that this material world even for immanent reasons could only have a finite duration. I think I was not mistaken in supposing that Nernst, as was usual with scientists of his generation, was not positively religious, and the conclusion seemed—and still seems—natural to me that in his frame of mind the everlasting universe had taken the place both of the eternal God and of the immortal soul. I did not feel tempted to take the attitude of an apologetic theologian here. On the question of personal immortality my own views were very definitely agnostic. I had realized the basic difference between the philosophical idea of an immortal soul and the New Testament's belief in a resurrection of the body. Their merging in many trends of Christian theology I had learnt to ascribe to the historical fact that much of Christian theology is an interpretation of the gospel by the concepts of Greek philosophy. This understanding of the historical origin of some of our most common religious beliefs had left me in an even more sceptical state of mind with respect to the traditional interpretation of religion than natural science alone might have done.

But what struck me about Nernst's view was this: even if immortality was desirable, what would it help a man who did not believe in the immortality of the rational soul or in the resurrection of the feeling person, to believe in the unending processes of nature instead? Would stars and atoms feel and think in his stead after the irrevocable death of the ego? I think, a deeply irrational trait of scientism was revealed in his view: the world had taken the place of God, and it was blasphemy to deny it God's attributes. Here was the place where I first realized that scientism contained an element which I now would call the secularization of Christian religion. This will be the theme of my next lecture.

Here I only add a few remarks on the particular importance of the question about the age of the universe for the dogmatics of scientism and of Christianity. I think, it may easily be seen rationally that this importance is overestimated on both sides, the main point being the irrational one of which I have been speaking.

Take scientism first. Western scientism does not seem to stick any more to dogmas about infinity. This was different in the 19th century. But western scientists have thoroughly learned the lesson of empiricism, and their dogmatism today is one of scientific method rather than of particular positive statements. The situation is different in the communist ideology. This ideology has not avoided the temptation of dogmatizing particular positive views. This fact became best known in the episode of the officially enforced non-Mendelian genetics which, I hope, now belongs to the past. But as far as I am informed the infinite duration of the world is still considered to be an irremovable part of dialectical materialism. Rationally seen, there does not seem to be an inherent necessity for this view in Marxism. Neither the deep insights of Marx on the importance of the material—i.e. of the economic—element in human history, nor the criticism of that philosophical attitude which is termed idealism in the Marxist language, seem to make this view logically necessary. I think the important elements of Marxist philosophy would be far more convincing to a modern mind if they were clearly separated from scientific dogmas that were modern in the lifetime of Marx and Engels and are out of date now.

This decision may well be left to those who have the right to decide what is true in Marxism. Yet I have felt tempted to ponder upon the reasons that make this modernisation of Marxism such a difficult task, and I have found three closely connected possible reasons. First, Marxism does have to play the rôle of religious dogma to its own believers, and religions always find it difficult to admit that they are not infallible; the fact that Marxism considers itself to be science does not seem to change this psychological problem. Second, I think there is a positive attraction of the traditional view to the Marxist mind, on lines very similar to those I described when speaking of Nernst; infinity is something like a symbol of the naturalist creed. Third, communism, being a fighting community and carrying on the doctrine of class conflict, considers it a political necessity to take a definite part in ideological controversies; and seeing that Christian churches consider the creation of the world in time to be a religious truth, communists are afraid of the detrimental political consequences of admitting that the Church may not just have been a bulwark of superstition in this respect.

If, however, we now turn to Christian theology, I do not see a rational necessity for Christians to believe that the world did have a beginning in time. As long as the text of the Bible was considered to be the ultimate authority even on scientific questions the situation was different. But this battle was decided in the time of Galileo, and today there are only very few Christian groups left that would read the relevant passages of the Bible like a scientific textbook. Christians today find no difficulty in admitting that the world is more than the mere six thousand years that a chronological evaluation of the Bible text would allow. So I do not see why it should be more Biblical to assume that the world is five thousand million years old than to assume that it has existed since an infinite time. Once you have reached the theological level of St. Augustine, saying that divine creation is not a process in time but an act by which even time is constituted, there seems to be no necessity that God should create a finite time rather than an infinite one. Neither do I share the view that science, considering the possibility that the world may have had a beginning in time, thereby contributes to the classical proof of the existence of God as the ultimate cause of the world. If I am right in thinking that there is no philosophical reason for extending the concept of time beyond the existing world, it will be consistent also to limit the concept of a cause to application within the world. If, admitting a beginning of the world, we see no meaning in the question what happened in the time before the world existed, we may see equally little meaning in asking what pre-existent thing caused the world to come into existence. Science fits in with religious agnosticism at least as well as with the dogma of creation.

Meditating about the reasons that make the idea of a beginning of the world in time so attractive to confessing Christians, I find the strict parallel to the reasons I suspected for the Marxist predilection for the opposite view. First, Christians, too, like to find their religion infallible in some points, especially after having suffered so many setbacks in the conflict with modern science. Second, the finite duration of the universe serves as something like a symbol of the Christian understanding of human history; and since I think this understanding is to be taken most seriously I want to return to this point in the next lecture. The third reason, being a reason of practical politics, may be less important with the Protestants of our time who have submitted to the liberal idea that religion and politics ought to be kept apart; in Roman Catholic circles another tradition is still alive to which such considerations are not altogether foreign.

If I am right in seeing this complete parallelism I think I am right in refusing to take sides in the material question of infinite time, at least so long as no strong scientific arguments can be produced. I think there is a slight advantage for the idea of a finite time, but probably the truth is different from everything we imagine today. The point that ought to concern us then is no longer what we believe on this question but what human attitude is expressed in a propensity for this or that belief. I have already touched on this question, and it will be one of the subjects of the next lecture.

10 *What is Secularization?*

QUITE naturally, our story has brought us back to the starting point, to the questions and concerns of our own time. The present lecture, the last of the first series, is to be devoted to a consideration of what we have learnt on our way through history.

First of all, I must say what this lecture is not meant to be.

To begin with, it raises no claim to provide any sort of therapy for the dangerous sufferings of the modern world. It is meant to be a contribution towards a diagnosis. Let me dwell on this medical metaphor for a moment. Therapy and diagnosis stand in a characteristically complementary relationship to each other. In therapy, the doctor must frequently make hasty decisions and carry them through with a firm hand; the sickness does not slacken its progress, and the patient is usually a weak man, who needs a halt to be made. Diagnosis, on the other hand, is hardly ever finished. It demands constant observation, imagination, self-criticism and unwearying patience, as the human organism is immensely complicated. It is unprincipled to begin therapy without having made the best possible diagnosis. But the best possible diagnosis at one moment is often enough not the final diagnosis; the diagnostic work must continue during therapy and often benefits decisively from the reactions of the sick man to therapy.

If humanity is the patient and its sickness consists in the crisis of the life of an epoch, no individual can be the doctor. Many try their hand at the cure.

Anyone who takes part in this attempt, alone or in a group, must know that therapy is only possible through resolute, clear and perspicacious action. This is true no matter whether the action be concerned with the education of the individual, the creation of advantageous social conditions, or high politics. If I may once again speak more personally here than is perhaps usual in academic lectures, I would say that such action seems to me to be absolutely necessary, and that I, together with other like-minded people, have been and continue to be ready for it. But it is not the aim of these lectures to suggest possible ways and means.

On the other hand, however, these lectures have not been given out of a purely theoretical interest, but out of just that pragmatic concern which is hinted at in the word diagnosis. How often have I found in educational, social and political groups and theories, engaged in furious disputes with one another, a sincere good-will, a deep concern for our whole future, and a readiness to give a great deal of active help, as well as the inevitable human weaknesses, on both sides. This observation once again confronts anyone who has once begun to free himself from the prejudices of his own group, with the horrifying question: "In that case, who has made the right diagnosis?" Further observation often enough shows that the competing diagnoses indeed contradict each other in formulation, but not so much in structure, and that each party in the dispute fails to understand not only the opposing party, but also itself, with any degree of accuracy. With this observation, the disputing parties themselves become patients instead of ostensibly being doctors: the diagnosis of their own condition becomes vitally important. Why can the doctors of our own age so seldom help themselves? Why do they not recognize their own illness? Considerations of this kind have moved me to the questions which I will put in this last lecture.

It therefore follows, secondly, that this lecture does not even claim to give the correct diagnosis of our age. Indeed, its immediate effect must be precisely the opposite; if it should have any truth in it, it can at first only make the putting forward of diagnoses more difficult. It seeks to recognize at a new level of reflection the common strengths and common weaknesses of those diagnostic modes of thought which deserve to be taken most seriously to day, namely, to use catch-phrases, the ecclesiastical, the liberal and the Marxist modes of thought. The hint that there is possibly such a plane of knowledge must suffice as our present aim.

The practical significance of this knowledge will not consist in the final establishment of the correct diagnosis in place of the false ones. It is much more likely that it could loosen the dependence of our therapeutic exertions on one-sided diagnostic theories, i.e. the dependence of our social and political attitudes on dogmatically maintained doctrines. Perhaps, however, I may be permitted to prepare the way in the present lecture for a completely different trend, not the trend towards practical work, indispensable though it is, but that towards a stricter kind of theory. The second series of these lectures is in fact meant to give not a historical, but a systematic examination of the basic concepts of modern science.

Finally, just one remark on the form of the lectures. As the even flow of a historical narrative, only occasionally flavoured with reflection, is now giving way to a more abstract train of thought, I am attempting to make the division of this and later lectures clearer by sub-titles and résumés of the content. The main theme of the present lecture is that of secularization. This will be introduced in section (A), and in section (B) applied to modern political revolutions as being the most important example of it. In (C), the ambivalence which we already discovered in the first lecture to be a mark of our contemporary faith in science will turn out to be a characteristic feature of secularization in general. I will follow it right back into early Christian history and rediscover it particularly in the Christian idea of chiliasm, the belief in a coming thousand-year reign of Christ on this earth. Section (D) will look for the chiliastic features in the modern belief in progress. The attempt to understand Marx will bring us to Hegel, who sketched out a basic pattern of historical understanding as a whole. This pattern, discussed in section (E), is ambiguous for us to a special degree: on the one hand it contains ideas which even our own analysis simply cannot abandon; on the other hand, it seems to be as it were the summit of that modern Titanism of which the faith in science of our days might almost be said to be just a harmless offspring. From this background in (F) I attempt to understand Marx, and in (G) once again return to the ambivalence of the success of the modern age.

Finally, in (H) I take advantage of this description of secularization to reflect one last time on its significance, on the one hand with the means of Christian theology, on the other in the light of modern science. This reflection should then clarify the philosophical significance of the transition to the systematic problems of natural science, as it shows how little it is possible to make any historical position, even if it be the position of the very science in which we ourselves believe, the unassailable starting point of all speculation.

A *The concept of secularization*

Let us first remind ourselves of the main stages in the course of these lectures up till now.

I began with the question "What does science mean for our time?" In connection with this question, I formulated two theses, which I now repeat for reconsideration:

1. Faith in science plays the rôle of the dominant religion of our time.
2. The relevance of science for our time can, at least today, only be evaluated in concepts which express an ambiguity.

I then proposed, as a limited contribution to the diagnosis of our time, a study of the historical origin of this faith in science. This was to centre on a special example, for which I selected the history of the concepts of creation and cosmogony.

First, I spoke of mythical cosmogonies which were at the

same time theogonies. I attempted to show how they united two elements which seem to us to be essentially different: a well-considered narrative of the physical origin of all things and the expression of an understanding of human existence. As the gods changed, so the two aspects of cosmogony changed. The God of the Jews taught his people to make a sharp distinction between good and evil, that is between life and death. Greek philosophy made a distinction between true and false, that is between being and non-being. I attempted to show how the Jewish and Greek ideas of the beginning of the world corresponded to the understanding of life and truth among both peoples. Then Christianity transformed pre-Christian nature: but the world which it had built was again transformed by modern reality. In modern times, scientific research took the place of an interpretation of the world by traditional symbols. I pursued the growth of a scientific cosmogony. This cosmogony ends, if it is expressed with scientific prudence, in open questions. This was evident in the case of the development of life, which we shall not really understand until we can give a better answer to the two questions, "What is life?" and "What is physics?" It was evident in the sphere of astronomy, where the infinity of space and time itself became an unsolved question. At the same time, however, we discovered that many people in our time hold quite firm convictions about these open questions, and we had occasion to assume that these convictions of theirs had their roots in their specific understanding of human existence. Precisely in its unresolved questions, cosmogony is evidently still a symbol of the way in which we understand the basic problems of human life. One of these interpretations is faith in science. Have we understood it better at the end of our course than we did before?

In the first lecture, I narrowed the scope of questions to make it more tractable. Now I must take the opposite step of making it more general. I shall no longer be asking about cosmogony, but about that of which it is merely a symbol. I must of necessity go about this generalizing without attempting a proof. History is too complicated to allow the strict proof of general assertions. I venture this generalizing as a diagnostic hypothesis.

I take up the two initial theses and replace them with more special ones:

1. The modern world can largely be understood as the result of a secularization of Christianity.
2. Secularization is an ambiguous word which describes an ambivalent process.

First of all, I must explain the words used in these sentences.

The word "secularization" derives from the Latin word *saeculum*, which means century. In traditional Christian language, *saeculum* means the time in which we are actually living today, as opposed to God's eternity: hence it also means everything which belongs to this world and which to that extent does not belong directly to God. Secularization was for a long time a juristic concept which designated the transference of ecclesiastical goods into secular hands. Thus men talked of a secularized monastery. In our century, many authors have begun to use the word secularization in a more general way as a description of the process by which the modern world has developed. This use of the word implies certain conceptions which I will discuss in detail; I will begin with some negative remarks.

If the modern world is the product of a process of secularization, it is not a religious world in the strict sense of the word. It is neither properly a Christian world nor is it the world of a new religion, replacing Christianity. It would, however, be equally impossible to describe it as a world totally devoid of any relationship with a religious world. A secularized monastery is the same building as before; its rooms still have the structure of monastic cells, a refectory and a chapel, even if they are now used for other purposes. Similarly, the modern world still has the structure of a Christian world; the drawing of the picture is as it were still Christian, even if all the colours have changed, even if black has changed into white and white into black, as in a photographic negative. If this is so, however, the process can only be ambivalent and the concepts in which we express it must necessarily have an ambiguous sound. For the problem is: Are we to stress the Christian structure, or the non-Christian use of it?

After this explanation of the terminology, I will give examples for the new theses.

One example is the origin of modern science, as we encountered it, for example, with Galileo. In the sixth lecture, I asserted that the concept of strict and generally valid laws of nature could hardly have arisen without the Christian concept of creation. Matter in the Platonic sense, which must be "prevailed upon" by reason, will not obey mathematical laws exactly: matter which God has created from nothing may well strictly follow the rules which its Creator has laid down for it. In this sense I called modern science a legacy, I might even have said a child, of Christianity. But then I had to show how science lost contact with its parental home. Children can experience the death of their parents.

We have already seen in Galileo's conflict with the Church the ambiguity of any concept which describes this process of secularization. Was Galileo right, when he read the greatness of God in the book of nature, in thinking that he was fulfilling God's will that men should read this book? Was the Church right in thinking that this would distract men from the will of God which stands written in the book of redemption? Using the categories of our century we could describe the positions as being equally ambivalent. If we leave aside the violent means which the Church used wrongly, and, in the long run, used unsuccessfully precisely because they were wrong—did the Church want to hinder the progress of knowledge, or did it require a wider field of vision than that of the fanatical specialist?

The concept of infinity offers another example. The majority of pre-Christian world-views knew only of a finite world. For Christian philosophy, the world was similarly finite, but God was infinite. In modern times, the world takes over this attribute of God: infinity becomes secularized. Under this aspect it is most remarkable that our century has begun to doubt the infinity of the world. I believe that in our time a critical examination of secularization is beginning at exactly the same time as secularization is achieving a consistency hitherto unknown.

B *The political revolutions*

In order to see the full weight of secularization, however, we should not limit ourselves to theories. Instead we should speak, for example, of politics. I therefore take up the thread where I let it go at the end of the fifth lecture. There I pointed to the Christian background of three modern phenomena: military obedience, ordered government and political revolution. Allow me now to develop the last of these three themes further.

At first glance, the political revolutions of Europe display many differences, and that should not surprise us, as history never repeats itself. I have spoken of the English Puritan revolution of the 17th century and of the French *grande révolution* of the 18th century. One difference is that the first of the two interpreted its aims in strictly Christian terms, whereas the second even went through a stage of militant opposition to Christianity. These two revolutions were not notably successful: the revolutionary governments collapsed, and in each case an age of restoration followed. As movements akin to them, which were at first sight more successful, I should mention the American revolution of the 18th century and the Russian revolution of the 20th: both erected systems of government which have lasted down to our time. These systems of government again differ from each other; anyone asserting that one was like the other in any essential feature would in fact win little political sympathy either in the western or in the eastern world. Despite everything, however, I regard it as historically true that all these revolutions, and similarly all the political systems which they set up, either immediately, or after several apparently abortive beginnings, have a great deal in common with each other, and I hope to trace just this common modern element in them.

It is the ambivalence intrinsic to modern civilizations which in my view makes it easy for these systems to regard themselves as being so different: each of them allows of opposed interpretations, each of which contains a good deal of truth.

In speaking in this way, I must, however, make my own standpoint quite clear. I belong to the western world. I share the western conception of political freedom and the rights of man. My remarks would be misunderstood were one to find in them a tendency to obliterate differences in approach to questions in which right and wrong is at stake. A decision is necessary, even if we see what is false on our side and what is true on the opposite side. But I fear that we squander the good consequences of such a decision if we allow the necessary decision, once made, to make us blind to the common feature of all modern systems. We are directed to live with one another in *one* world. Just when we rightly and passionately hope that systems hostile to our own will develop to the standards of humanity which we hold to be the only permissible ones, just at this point, we may not identify these standards with our own historical prejudices and with our own highly ambiguous actions. If self-control is a prerequisite of any ordered conduct in human life, those at least who possess the necessary gifts of understanding and factual knowledge ought to exercise this intellectual self-control in their views about the side which they have chosen as their own in the present historical struggle. This attitude is not only a requisite of good taste: there could come moments in which survival depended on our being capable of it.

I am thus putting forward the supposition that revolutions have very much in common. Let me take the slogans of the French Revolution as a starting point: Freedom, Equality, Brotherhood. If I see it rightly, these words express a common aspiration of all these different revolutionary movements. The distribution of emphasis may have varied. Perhaps Cromwell's Ironsides tried above all to obtrude their understanding of brotherhood, Robespierre's Jacobins their understanding of freedom, and Lenin's Bolsheviks their understanding of equality on their fellow men. But as soon as we take the three concepts as seriously as they deserve, they do not allow of separation. Can we speak of true freedom as long as it rests on the servitude of part of society? If not, freedom also demands equality. Can we maintain equality by brute force? If not, equality rests on brotherhood. Can I honestly call my neighbour my brother if I do not accord him the freedom I claim for myself? If not, brotherhood demands that a fellow man be permitted his freedom.

C *The Christian background to the modern ambivalence*

The brief analysis of the three basic revolutionary concepts which I have just given was, I think, a Christian analysis. In this sense all modern revolutions have sought to realize Christian demands. But why have they then so forgotten their Christian background that in the most recent of these revolutions it has been felt impossible for the same man to be both a Communist and a Christian at the same time?

If I see things correctly, this progressive amnesia on the part of revolutions corresponds to a quite similar forgetfulness on the part of official Christianity. In the fifth lecture, I spoke of the intrinsic ambivalence of Christian history itself, and sought to describe it by means of the concepts of radical and conservative Christianity. The earliest Church was radical, but not in a political sense. As the success of Christianity brought political life within the purview of Christians, there gradually developed the medieval Church, which in a comprehensive, a catholic way embraced both the radical and the conservative elements.

This catholicism did not mean peace: it meant the incessant strife of the opposed tendencies within the Church, and this strife means life. In modern times the strife has torn apart the catholic unity. The Reformation divided the Church into disputing churches, and secularization divided the world into an official Christianity which tends towards pure conservatism and a non-Christian world whose radicalism no longer understands itself in the light of the Gospel.

If we consider in detail the steps which have led here, today's conditions must seem to be the natural consequence of a necessary development. It is to make that quite clear that I have devoted so many lectures to an extremely specialized problem. But if we look back from our present position to the beginnings of Christianity, the result must seem paradoxical, self-contradictory to the point of absurdity. Let me analyze these self-contradictions.

The Church preserves this most revolutionary document of human history, the Gospel, the truth of which is slowly slipping from the consciousness of the citizen of our modern world. As the Church knows that what it preserves is the truth, it allows itself to be led into the attitude which is assumed by all who preserve supreme good against the changing trends of the day: it allows itself to be seduced into conservatism. At least we will hand down uncorrupted to future generations the good with which we have been entrusted! Laudable as this conservative attitude is, the facts of life force it towards a position which is not so very different from the equally laudable and equally inadequate position of the Scribes and Pharisees. And as usual this is seen much more easily from outside than from within. The Christian concept of the Pharisee, applied to the Church itself, might easily be the last Christian concept the modern world forgets.

Even the person who sees this from the inside cannot *ipso facto* alter it. Despite many still wonderful works and achievements of Christians throughout the world, and despite some hectic exertions on the part of Church officials to keep pace with modern times, the Church has for several centuries no longer been leading the historical process; it can hardly still follow it. The most profound thought possible within Christian conservatism is therefore probably that the Church should not in any way lead the process of history; indeed it should not even follow it, as this process is self-destructive, or at least alien to the Gospel. Where this voice has a genuine ring we may not ignore it. But I fear that even it expresses only one side of the truth, and not the complete truth. I feel that it too remains within the sphere of ambivalence, and the consequence of an undetected ambivalence in one's own attitude is blindness to the facts.

The modern world, however, is no less blind. Take one more look at the revolution. *La révolution dévore ses enfants.* We know how blind violent insurgents are to what they really achieve. Did the Ironsides bring brotherhood? Did the Jacobins bring freedom? Did the Bolsheviks bring equality? I give no answer to these questions, not even a negative one, as even this straightforwardness, judged by the later course of history, would probably be an exaggeration. I would, however, ask: Why this ambivalence of revolutions? Has it perhaps something to do with an age-old dilemma, well known from Christian history, that of violence and non-violence?

The aim of the three revolutions of which I have just spoken was a state of society in which rule by force would no longer be necessary, whether this state of society was given the name of the Fifth Monarchy, the Age of Reason or the classless society. But the way taken by the revolution to this supersession of force is, in fact, force. Of course the thoughtful leaders of the revolution will argue that the ruling power can never be overthrown except by force. Here the leaders of the revolution are expressing a well-known conservative view of human nature. In all previous history those men have ruled who were ready and able to defend their rule by force. It is perhaps the most revolutionary idea of revolutions that this need not always be so. This idea derives from Christian eschatology. But is the revolution that fights for this idea the sole power in history that is justified in using force? Or does it thereby sacrifice its aim to the devilry of the means which it regards as necessary?

This dilemma of revolutions seems to me to throw a special

light on the thesis of the mutual blindness of Christianity and the modern world. Christianity does not recognise its own concern in revolutions and is thrown on a fruitless defensive. But revolution sees Christianity only as the guardian of what must perish and therefore forfeits the possibility of understanding its own concern with the aid of concepts which reach deeper than those which it can itself offer. I am therefore attempting once again to portray the dilemma here as it has revealed itself in Christian history—which must be regarded as pre-history to modern revolutions.

In Christianity, the relationship between the end and the means is less simple than in its pagan precursors. In Christian terms, paganism divinized human nature and along with it its intrinsic tendency to use force: this can be seen even in so spiritual a creation as Plato's model state and in a form of government as rooted in ethics as that of the Stoic emperors of the 2nd century. Christ completely rejected the divinization of our natural habits. In the coming kingdom of heaven the rule of these demons will be broken. But, asked the following Christian era, how will the kingdom of God come? It does not come through our efforts: it comes of its own power. This thought contains a deep insight into human existence, which finds its application in daily life. If the demons are conquered, they do not succumb to our efforts of will, but to an operation which we can experience only as a gift of grace. This, however, does not in the least dispense us from any exertion of our will at all. Grace is the answer to our longing for grace, and this longing is not in earnest unless it leads to the most determined personal effort. It is a well-known doctrine that man cannot give himself grace but that he can squander the grace that is offered. This is in accord with the teaching of the Fourth Gospel, that judgment takes place in this life. Should things be otherwise in the great course of world history? But what would this mean for world history?

The final victory over the rule of force is the Last Judgment, the Second Coming of Christ. The orthodox Christian teaching was that no human action could influence the time of his Second Coming. In the present span of time, in which we live in this expectation, we should attempt to live as citizens of his coming kingdom. How this was to be done in practice was, however, the question which produced the tension between radical and conservative Christianity, and I expressed the view that this very tension was the driving force of world history in the Christian era.

This tension has at times expressed itself in a subtle point of dispute within the Christian theology of history. The Revelation of St. John speaks of a thousand-year kingdom of Christ and his saints before a new heaven and a new earth are finally made. What did this millennium represent? The present era of the Christian Church? Could this confused time be regarded as a rule of Christ and his saints? Or was the thousand-year kingdom yet to come, perhaps soon, perhaps still within the lifetime of the present generation? Did its coming perhaps still depend on our acting rightly? This belief, that it would come soon and that we ought to act accordingly, was called chiliasm (*chilia ete* = a thousand years); the Church regarded it as heresy, but many social revolutionaries of the late Middle Ages and early modern times took it over. But chiliasm itself revealed the dilemma: How then should we act to help to bring in the kingdom? Will the rule of non-violence be brought about by non-violence or by violence?

Only a few have at any time attempted really to live according to the Sermon on the Mount. For a long time, the recognised form of this attempt was the life of the monk. In a characteristic fashion, the great prophet of chiliasm in the early 13th century, Joachim of Fiore, taught that there were three Churches following one after the other: the Church of the patriarchs in the Old Testament, founded on Abraham; the Church of the priests from the time of Christ's first coming, founded on Peter, and the Church of the monks, now beginning, founded on John. Alien as this way of speaking is to us today, it is the spiritual tradition in which the European revolutions still live. Joachim expected the coming of the new kingdom through God's rule over history; but man had to live according to this kingdom if he and the brothers who would be reached by his voice and his example were to share in it and not fall into damnation. For this hope, the "Spirituals" of the Franciscan order, among others, deeply influenced by Joachim, made any sacrifice, including that of their lives. Later, in the Protestant world, the natural form of the attempt to live strictly after Christ's commandment was the sect. The most splendid example of what a life lived according to the unqualified Sermon on the Mount can achieve, and one that is most visible to modern eyes, is that of the Quakers. The Church was indeed often right in the face of the exalted expectations and fantastic scriptural interpretations of the "enthusiasts", but any glance at the past or the present will show that "enthusiast" is also an eminently convenient formula for doing down those who attempt to take Christianity seriously.

When I said that the European revolutions still lived in the spiritual tradition of chiliasm, I did not primarily have to think of those who renounced a violent contribution to the coming of the kingdom, but of the chiliastic social revolutionaries. Important as this distinction is, however, belief in an imminent radical change in world history is common to both sides. A secularized form of this belief governs the stormy course of modern history.

D *Belief in progress*

The one tenet of faith which the western world today shares with Communism—and, moreover, with the nationalist movements of non-European countries—is a belief in progress. This is a recent idea in history. Neither European antiquity nor the great cultures of the East understand history as a field of progress. For the Christian Church, there was only a progress in history which had already taken place, the first coming of Christ, and a second progress in the future, the end of history in his coming again. But chiliasm allowed a transposition of this otherworldly salvation of history into the history in the midst of which we live. From a historical point of view, I regard belief in progress as a secularized chiliasm. Of course modern man would understand chiliasm in the opposite way, as a dawn of the belief in progress, still verging on the mythical. Be this as it may, only the religions of the Judaeo-Christian tradition seem to have the concept of an unrepeatable history of our world, and I would not regard it as fortuitous that the modern concept of history has arisen in a Christian culture. Were I to return to the philosophical problems, I would at this point have to investigate the Christian and the modern concepts of time. I hope I might be able to make it probable that our concept of history is not less, but to a still greater degree, a legacy of Christianity to the modern world than is our concept of the law of nature. But that would take me too far afield today. I will now investigate the particular understanding of progress in various modern political systems.

The western world understands its own scale of values to be one which preserves what was good in the Christian tradition; it therefore finds little difficulty in linking its belief in progress with Christian conceptions. The central political idea of the West is the freedom of the individual, and without doubt Christianity has taught us to take any living human being seriously as a person, no matter to what class, race or nation he or she belongs. Liberalism might well claim for itself that it took Christian convictions seriously in advancing this respect for the person in the political sphere as well, often against the resistance of conservative Christians. Even technical progress can, at least by way of the natural science depicted in these lectures, be linked with Christianity: technical science can understand its work as the fulfilment of the commandment "subdue the earth under you". The problems of the modern world, with which I began in the first lecture, can then well be understood as a consequence of the ambiguity of a secularized Christian world. But this thought itself contains an ambiguity which I must investigate in detail at the end. Before this, however, I must turn to the apparently expressly anti-religious doctrines of Marxism. If we are to do them justice, we must allow ourselves to be led on to a new plane of historical understanding.

I would express and advocate the by no means original view that in some very important points Marx was nearer to Christianity than the committed Christians against whom he turned. I can only develop this view in two stages. Marx is only to be understood as one who trod a way opened by Hegel. I must therefore turn first to Hegel, as much for his own sake as for his significance for Marx and Marxism.

E *Hegel*

I am not concerned here with Hegel's perhaps all too artificial and untenable particular theses. The time in which we had to fight our way free of Hegel's influence, natural scientists, philosophers and theologians alike, is past. I should like to show which way of thought was only made possible by Hegel's approach to the question of philosophy. One can call Hegel the first philosopher who regarded history as a philosophical problem. The central theoretical problem can easily be elucidated by a retrospective glance at these lectures. When I spoke of views of the origin of the world, I had always two simultaneous questions in mind: Why did men believe this or that in this or that phase of human history? and, Which of these views has shown itself to be true? If we take both questions equally seriously, we are brought into a confusing situation. We ourselves live in a particular phase of history. My present theme, that of secularization, may be described by the question "Why has our own age the views which it in fact has?" But if I thus make our own views historically comprehensible, where is our naive faith in the truth of these views? And if I make a radical reduction of truth to historical relativities, what do I mean when I declare my own views, e.g. just this historical relativism, to be true?

It is indeed so easy to show how well historical relativism fits the thought-pattern of modern times; i.e. it is so easy to explain it itself in the frame of historical relativity. In this morass of historical relativities, where can we still take a firm step? Hegel was the first thinker to understand this question, and he sketched an answer. Perhaps I may indicate this answer in simplified expressions, beginning by leaving aside an explicit use of Hegel's central concept of the Absolute. According to Hegel, truth is not real otherwise than in the form of historical positions following one another: each of these positions is to some extent the truth. But it is only the truth to some limited extent. The dialectical process of history is maintained by each position showing itself to be one-sided once it has prevailed. Therefore truth itself now demands a new, contradictory, position, which supersedes the previous one only to suffer the same fate after its own victory. In this constant change, the truth which was there in previous stages is at the same time both superseded and preserved; to use Hegel's intentionally ambiguous expression, it is "taken up"[1] in the later stages. If we keep to this quite general understanding of Hegel's, and leave on one side his artificial systematization of history (instructive as it is in individual points), we shall have described what is probably the only way that we too can follow. I have in fact constantly used this mode of thought in the previous lectures. I believe that it can also be applied consistently to our own position in history. Even this application I hint at here only in a somewhat superficial way, but one which will perhaps be sufficient to use for the moment. As far as certain ideas reveal themselves inescapably to our honest, self-critical urge towards the truth, as being true, we shall be justified in using them as a basis for our judgments. Should the future set them aside,[2] we can do nothing about it: but we may trust that the element of truth in them will be preserved. Otherwise a man who has recog-

[1] German: *aufgehoben*. The verb can mean "take up", "preserve" or "abolish"; it is impossible to reproduce the word-play in English.

[2] *aufheben*, see note 1.

nized that he stands in the midst of history could hardly pass judgment on his own thought.

But this last remark compels us at one, equally well known, point to criticize Hegel, at least to criticize the picture which his philosophy presented and had to present to his time. His own thought claims to be a system, and it must be so, intending to think the Absolute. But "the absolute is the result"; Hegel did not at least stand in the way of the impression that it is Hegel's philosophy which is this absolute result of the history of the spirit. Understood in this way, his philosophy appears as the most titanic chiliasm there has ever been. The word chiliasm is in place here. Hegel understood his philosophy as the genuine understanding of Christianity: this problem of understanding Christianity was his starting point in his youth. The definitive understanding of Christianity is, however, the millennium. Thus, even in Hegel's political philosophy, the early 19th century state was not to be distinguished from the millennium with complete clarity. (It is, however, unjust to ascribe this view to him in the particular case of the Prussian state in which he lived for his last years; he was not uncritical of this state, though careful in his expressions, and one might more accurately call him a philosopher of the French Revolution.)

F *Marx*

Here we reach the point at which Marx criticized Hegel. Marx was a real Hegelian. He believed, perhaps in the last resort more literally than Hegel himself, in a final stage of history. But this stage had not been achieved—how could people assert its presence when one thought of the fearful social conditions which the beginning of the industrial revolution brought with it? And it was to be achieved, not by further thought, but by action. Hegel seemed to have dissolved history into a charade of spirits, called ideas. To describe the complete reversal of thought which is necessary for philosophy, he coined the somewhat mysterious maxim that the philosopher must learn to walk on his head. Marx boasted that while philosophy itself had been standing on its head in Hegel's writings, he had once again set it on its feet. The feet are Marx's economic ideas. Now whatever may have been ill-considered or false in the details of Marx's economic theory, he stressed a most important and, I would say, a most Christian truth. One of Jesus' terrifying remarks is that it is easier for a camel to go through the eye of a needle than for a rich man to enter into the kingdom of God.[1] Marx understood the truth from which this remark derives. He understood it in secularized form and may have exaggerated it, but he understood it. "Where your treasure is, there will your heart be also";[2] that is the irrefutable truth behind Marx's conviction that history is guided by economic conditions and that anyone who would alter the life of man must alter economic conditions. How many committed Christians understand this truth? In the question of the appropriate means of bringing about economic and social changes, however, it seems to me that Marxism was open to the ambivalence that is my theme. Marx himself was somewhat ambiguous in this respect. On the one hand, he believed in the necessity of history; he believed in the inevitable coming of the classless society in the same way as Christians believe in the inevitable coming of the Last Judgment. Perhaps one can even say that his teaching gained so many adherents because he offered a positive, though secularized, eschatology at a time when Christians no longer believed firmly in their own eschatology and thus aroused the justifiable impression that the foundations of their faith were affected with doubt. In contrast, Marx preached action; he did not expect history to progress otherwise than through men themselves. The question of the right means of action led to the division of the International Socialist Movement into those who believed in an evolution within the framework of parliamentarian democracy and those who felt it was necessary for the existing order of society to be overthrown

[1] Mark 10. 25. [2] Luke 12. 34.

by force. Decisions about the means do not remain without influence on aims. Today, the gulf separating communism from western Socialism is hardly less deep than that separating it from pure capitalism. Whether these two gulfs can ever be closed if the ambivalences in the present attitudes of all sides are better realized, we cannot decide today.

G *The ambivalence of success*

I leave the ambiguities of the aims and means of revolutions and turn once again to the ambivalence of their success. Earlier, I distinguished revolutions which were immediately successful from those which were not. On closer investigation, this turns out to be a superficial distinction. In one sense, all revolutions achieve their aims. The restoration of the Stuarts and the Bourbons lasted just long enough to make it clear that the past would never return. In another sense none of these revolutions achieved its aim. The final result of the English revolution was not the kingdom of God, but representative democracy. Neither Rousseau's return to nature nor the Age of Reason developed from the French and American revolutions, but the irrational dynamic of the civilization of the industrial age. Communism has so far brought into being not the classless society, but a highly successful hierarchy of functionaries and specialists. Modern competitive societies are much nearer each other in their actual conditions than in their programmes. Henry Ford's well-known view that the solution of the social question lies in increased production appears today as the practical doctrine of salvation of the Russian communists, while in capitalist countries a managerial class is tacitly suppressing independent entrepreneurs. Human life is planned to an unprecedented extent. Full employment, a free week-end, technical appliances and amusements for all are generally the sought-after ideals, industrialization and birth control the pressing problems, nuclear war, *1984* and the *Brave New World* the nightmares of this society. And its prevailing common faith is, as I said in the first lecture, faith in science. But this faith is deeply ambiguous. If it keeps to the truth, as according to its own basic doctrine it must, it must concede that it has not understood man's nature and that it does not know where progress will take us.

H *What is secularization?*

We have come full circle; we find ourselves back at the starting point. We will attempt some final reflections on the results.

I chose a strong expression for the ambiguities of our time in saying that while the Church was blind to the true nature of modern times, the modern world was equally blind to its own nature. Both are blind to the significance of secularization. I said that the modern world was the result of a secularization of Christianity. That means that the modern world in certain respects is, and in certain respects is not, a Christian world. Contrary to the beliefs of many Christians and all secularists, I tend to the view that the modern world owes its uncanny success to a great extent to its Christian background. If the men who think that Christianity rests on the deepest insight into human nature which has yet been revealed to us in history are right, this view should not surprise us. To repeat it in traditional Christian language: the gods of nature have been vanquished by the God whom Christians call Our Father; therefore man, as God's son, has received power over nature. As he is son and not servant, he is free, and his freedom includes the freedom to act against the will of his Father, the God of love. He can now subject the world to himself, and secularism does precisely this. (In these last sentences I have followed as faithfully as possible Friedrich Gogarten's theology of secularization.)

But these thoughts need expansion. We must go one stage further in their Christian interpretation and then we must consider them once again from the modern side.

It may be helpful for a Christian theologian to imagine secularism as a Christian heresy. According to the theological definition, heresy (*hairesis*) is to take (*hairein*) a partial truth from the whole of the Christian truth and to make this part absolute. A heretic is a Christian, but an erring Christian. Different varieties of secularism select different aspects of Christianity; I will refrain from going into the details of these aspects. All select the truth that this world is to be changed, a truth which Jesus elucidated in his parables by such different examples as that of the grain of mustard-seed growing into a tree in which many birds can build their nests and that of the all-consuming fire. The modern world is a tree in which many birds build their nests, and it is an all-consuming fire. It is, I say once again, ambivalent. But it is heretical, i.e. blind to the other side of the truth, because it is blind to its own ambivalence. Belief in progress is a half-truth. Jesus clearly described the inevitability of ambivalence in the parable of the wheat and the tares, which grow together and will only be separated at the end. I have never seen a clearer description of modern times than this growing corn-field, in which the tares unavoidably grow up alongside the wheat. But he who sees the fact of this ambivalence has taken the first step away from it; he is forsaking the error that made him a heretic. Anyone, on the other hand, who does not see the ambiguity has fallen a hopeless victim to it.

Now I must turn the tables once again. It is not sufficient to call secularism a Christian heresy. One usually thinks of a heresy as the selection of part of a recognized totality of truth. The theologian who speaks of heresy is generally convinced that the Church possesses the all-embracing ("catholic") truth. This conception probably does not even describe the celebrated heresies of the past at all accurately. As a rule, the heretics stressed a side of Christianity which the Church had not taken seriously enough. Many of the Church's dogmatic decisions were called forth by heresies, and I think that the best dogmatic decisions of ancient times had a truly paradoxical character because they incorporated a truth brought to light by heresy in a thought-system which was using an apparently contradictory language. Be this as it may, secularization forces us to attempt a new interpretation of the Christian faith. This new interpretation has been going on for centuries, but it is by no means completed.

I have been at pains throughout these lectures to take account of this new interpretation. True, I have attempted to speak of ancient times in their own language, but I have also attempted to make it clear on each occasion that this was a language of times long gone by, a language which could perhaps express truths which many of us have forgotten or never learnt, but not a language which we moderns can honestly speak of as our own. I have treated many time-honoured religious views as myths or legends and have not attempted to conceal my agnosticism in the case of others. But my concern was not what is often called in modern theology the "demythologizing" of Christianity. As I myself have spent the greater part of my life in surroundings influenced more by natural science than by the Church, I feel the battle of demythologizing to have been decided long ago, perhaps in Galileo's days: it only remains for us to be honest in its consequences. Science has come into being and will, to judge by human standards, endure; in face of it there remains only the task of interpreting Christianity in a way credible to a thought schooled in it. I have attempted this task just as many other modern thinkers inside and outside theology have attempted it. What really concerns me is another question.

I touched on this question in my remarks about Hegel, and I must now outline it more precisely. Modern thought expresses itself most coherently in science. But we have no occasion to take science itself as an absolute truth. This holds in every detail. It is indeed virtually the most imposing feature of science that it requires of its disciples that they should be ready at every moment to re-examine even the most generally accepted scientific doctrines. The life of true science is a life of constant self-correction. This must be true still more in respect of the scientific attitude to the wide areas of human life in which science, as we know, does not, at least today, have the answer to the burning questions. And how sure are we of the general philosophical background to science?

If the views of secularization advanced here are correct, they give us additional information which at first sight will not lessen our embarrassment. If these views are correct, modern science would not perhaps have been possible without Christianity. In that case, we are evidently moving in a circle. We explain Christianity in concepts which are to be comprehensible to scientific thought: a thought which for its part is found itself to be a product of Christianity. But any thought which has become conscious of the relevance of history must move in a circle of this sort. Today we can reach a stage of consciousness at which the historical naivety of those who identify their own standpoint with absolute truth must vanish away. Once we have understood this, we are none the worse for it, for no one will be expected to base his judgments on anything but what he can know. We now understand only our task of constant self-correction better than before. If we are philosophers, of course, we shall have a concept of truth which accords with this stage of consciousness.

A philosophy which tries to achieve what is required by this stage of consciousness will presumably have to describe the circle of the mutual dependence of our concepts more than once. Perhaps I may be allowed to remark here that in my earlier lectures on the history of nature I attempted to describe a semi-circle of this movement. There I took the concepts of natural science for granted and attempted to show how human history grows out of the history of nature. In the series of lectures now ended I have described a second semi-circle. Here I have taken for granted the concepts of human history and attempted to show how modern natural science has grown out of human history. In the following series of lectures I shall venture on the first semi-circle for the second time. There, my theme will again be scientific statements about nature. But I shall not then simply accept them: I shall analyse their significance in the light of what we have learnt in the first semi-circle. That means that we must return to completely abstract questions. I am sorry about that, as I feel, as I am sure you do, that the now so frequently mentioned human problems are the burning ones. But one may not neglect analysis, and I would not feel myself up to any further analysis of the history of our time if I had not first made a critical examination of the concepts of our science, the tools in the workshop of modern rationality.

Acknowledgements

Index

Acknowledgements

Acknowledgement is made to the authors and publishers for quotations used from the following sources: *The Babylonian Epic of Creation*, verse translation by S. Langdon, The Clarendon Press; Hesiod's *Theogony*, prose translation by H. G. Evelyn-White, Heinemann & Co. Ltd.; *The Elder or Poetic Edda*, verse translation by Olive Bray, 1908; *The Younger Edda*, prose translation by Rasmus Anderson, 1880; Plato's *Parmenides*, translation by G. S. Kirk and J. E. Raven in *Presocratic Philosophers*, C.U.P.; *Plato's Cosmology: The Timaeus*, translation by F. M. Cornford, Routledge & Kegan Paul.

Index

Abraham, 18, 47f., 50
Absolute, Hegelian, 174f.
absolutism, royal, 93
acceleration, 104, 105, 118
Adam, 50, 53
age: of earth, 142f.; of universe, 146f.
ageing, and evolution, 134
aggregation, states of, 60
agnosticism, religious, 13, 22, 155
Alexander the Great, 28
allegory, 86
ambiguity/ambivalence: Christian background of, 166f.; of Christian history, 81, 90f.; contemporary, 177; in relevance of science, 12, 19; of revolutions, 168; and secularization, 159, 163ff.; of scientism, 18, 21f.; of success, 177f.
amino-acids, 135
Ampère, A. M., 12
Ansar, 28
Antichrist, 83
Anu, 28
ape, as man's ancestor, 135
Apsû, 28ff., 35, 55
Aquinas, *see* Thomas
Arab world, 13
Arche, 55
archetype(s), 68, 71, 72, 88
Archimedes, 103
Aristarchus of Samos, 64, 94, 97, 98
Aristotle, 54, 56, 73, 76, 88, 89, 95, 101, 104, 105, 122, 127, 129, 130, 131, 132
Assur, 38
Assurbanipal, 28, 38
Assyrians, 38
astronomy, and cosmogony, 64, 102f.
atomism: ancient, 60ff.; and cosmogony, 63f., 114f.; and mathematics, 69f.; and necessity, 75
atoms, radioactive, decay of, 142
Augustine, St, 86ff., 90, 150, 155
Avignon, Papal residence at, 91

Babylon, 27ff., 38, 47
Bach, J. S., 102
beginning of world, 73, 150; nature of, 36, 55
being, and forms, 57ff., 62f.
belief, meaning of term, 14
Bellarmine, St Robert, 110, 111
Benedict, St, 84
Bentley, Richard, 75, 120, 126, 127
Bestla, 32
Bethe, H. A., 151
birth control, 18, 19
bishops, 91, 93
blasphemy, 17
Bohr, Niels, 136, 138

Index

Bolthorn, 32
Bor, 32
Boyle, Sermons, 24
Brahe, Tycho, 99, 101
brain, electronic, 22, 139
brain-washing, 23
breath, 52
Buddhism, 22
buoyancy, 105
Buri, 32

calculators, electronic, 22, 139
carbon cycle, 151
causality: and evolution, 128; and finality, 129ff.; and motion, 105f.; and myth, 41
causes, four, 129f.
change, 59ff., 69
Chaos, 30, 36, 46
charity, *see* love
chiliasm, 159, 170ff.; and belief in progress, 172; and Hegel, 175
China, 13, 19
Christ, Second Coming of, 169f.
Christianity, 13, 77ff., 90ff.; and beginning of world, 155f.; conservative and radical, 83f., 94, 112, 166ff.; demythologizing of, 180; early interpretations, 85ff.; modern reinterpretations, 90f., 180; and modern science, 180f.; and myth, 78; and progress, 171f.; and revolutions, 169; secularization of, 162ff.
circle, veneration of, 99f.
Clarke, Samuel, 121, 122f.
classification, 45, 127
clergy, and truth, 15f.
Cluny, 91
comets, 119
communism: and Christianity, 155, 166; current practice of, 177; and dogmatization of particular views, 155; and western socialism, 177
Communist Party, 15
Confucianism, 22
consciousness, and machines, 140
Copernicus, Nicolaus, 22, 94, 98ff., 110
cosmogony: atomism and, 63f.; and creation, 24; and Greek philosophy, 54ff.; modern views, 142ff.; and ontology, 56; stellar motions and, 102f.
covenant, God's, 47ff.
creation: Augustine and, 86f.; continuous, 148f.; and cosmogony, 24ff.; direct, science and, 136; *ex nihilo*, 55, 76, 86f., 149; second, 79
Cronos, 30f.
Cuvier, 127
cybernetics, 138

Darwin, Charles, 128, 133f.
Debye, F., 151
decision, 78, 165
demiourgos, Plato's, 68, 73f., 76, 88, 120
Democritus, 60, 62f., 65
demythologization, 50, 180
Descartes, René, 65, 101, 102, 106, 113ff.; cosmology of, 116f.
diagnosis: need of, 20; of own condition, 158; relation to therapy, 157f.
dialectical materialism; and duration of world, 154; not science, 15
dictatorship, 20
divinization, of human nature, 169

Ea, 28, 29, 30, 35
earth: age of, 142ff.; atomist view, 64f.; motion of, 94ff.; sphericity of, Greeks and, 64
ecliptic, 97
economics, and history, 176
Edda, 27, 31f.
Einstein, A., 122, 145, 147
ellipse, 99, 101, 102, 114
Emperor and Pope, contest, 91
energy, conservation of, 115, 149
Engels, Friedrich, 154
Enlil, 38
enthusiasm, 171
Epic of Creation, Babylonian, 27ff.
Epicurus, 60, 66
epicycle, 99
Erebus, 30
Eros, 30, 70
eschatology, Marxist, 176
ethics: and religion, 16f.; of technology, 17; *see also* morality
Eudoxus, 97
Europe, and Christianity, 84
evil: as non-being, 75f.; origin of, 75, 87; *see also* good and evil
evolution, 126ff., 141; alternatives to, 141; possible limitations, 135f.; properties promoting, 133f.
experience: nature of, 77f.; and religion, 77f.; and science, 77f.

fairy-tales, 33
faith: Abraham and, 48; Christianity and, 79; nature of, 14, 48; and science, 12, 14f., 111
fall, the, 53
Faraday, Michael, 12
fetishes, 51
finality, 128f., 130ff.
flying saucers, 141
force: meaning of, 105; revolutions and, 168
Ford, Henry, 177
form(s), Platonic, 68f., 71f., 87f., 129; Augustine and, 88f.
Franciscans, 91
freedom: and Christianity, 177; and equality, 166; human, 19
Freeman, Kathleen, 63
Freud, Sigmund, 23
friction, 105

galaxy (-ies), 124, 144, 148, 149; age of, 146; dynamics of, 147
Galileo, 101, 103ff., 111, 163; and the Inquisition, 110
Genesis, 27, 42ff., 49, 50, 52f.; Augustine on, 86
genetics, communism and, 154
Geneva Conference, on uses of atomic energy, 15
geometry, 63, 116f.
Germany, 91
Ginungagap, 31, 36
God: atomists and, 65f.; Jewish view of, 47f.; Kant and, 124f.; of the philosophers, 52; in Plato, 68, 72f.; science and, 22; spirituality of, 50ff.; and time, 87; world as, 153
gods: meaning of, 37, 39; origin of, 35, 36; of the philosophers, 52; psychological interpretation, 38f.
Goebbels, J., 23
Gogarten, Friedrich, 178
Good, Form of the, 71f., 87f.
good and evil: Plato's view, 74; separation of, 48, 53

Index

grace, 169
gravity, law of, 118, 124
Gregory the Great, St, 84

half-life, 142
Hammurabi, 28
Hegel, G. W. F., 159, 173ff.
Heisenberg, W., 136
heresy, secularism as, 178f.
Hesiod, *Theogony*, 27, 30f., 54
Hipparchus, 95, 101
history: Christianity and, 79ff., 90f., 172; dialectical view of, 174f.; and the fall, 53; Jewish theology of, 50; philosophy and, 171f.
Hönir, 32
hope, and judgment, 80f.
Hoyle, Fred, 148
Huxley, T. H., 128
Huygens, Christian, 103, 115
hydrogen, 146

Iceland, 31
idea, 69, 88; *see also* form(s)
idealism, Marxist criticism, 154
idols, man-shaped, 51
immortality of the soul, 152f.
Incarnation, 107
indeterminacy, and natural law, 132
India, 13
indiscernibles, identity of, 122
individual, freedom of, 172
inertia, law of, 96, 105f., 117f., 122
infinity, secularization of concept, 163f.
information theory, 137
International, Socialist, 176
Iphigenia, 66
Isaac, 48
Isaiah, 51
Italy, 91

Jesuits, 109
Jesus, 77, 179; *see also* Christianity
Jews, 40; Babylonian captivity, 47; separation of, 48; *see also* Judaism
Joachim of Fiore, 170f.
Judaism, 79f.
judgment, 80f., 169
Jung, C. G., 38

Kant, Immanuel, 24f., 65, 102, 123ff., 132, 133, 143; cosmogony of, 121, 123ff.
Kepler, Johannes, 22, 101ff., 110, 117, 118, 119, 121; first law of, 101, 113f.
kings, divine right of, 93f.
Kingu, 30
Kisar, 28
knights, orders of, 93
knowledge, limits of, 145
kosmos, meaning, 26
Kuiper, G., 143

Lahamu and Lahmu, 28
Lamarck, 128
Langdon, S., 28
Laplace, Pierre Simon de, 25, 124
laws of nature, 14f., 65, 75, 120, 130f.; constancy of, 142f.; and creation, 163; and human laws, compared, 132; and myth, 41
Leibniz, 121ff., 131
Leucippus, 60, 65
liberalism, 172
life: evolution of, 126ff., *see also* evolution; expectation of, 18;

extra-terrestrial, 141f.; origin of, 135f.; physics/chemistry and, 136
Linnaeus, 45
Locke, John, 88
Lodur, 32
love, and Christianity, 79f., 92
Loyola, St Ignatius, 93
Lucretius, 60, 63, 66

Mach, Ernst, 122
machines: and consciousness, 140; relation to man, 138; self-reproduction, 139; spontaneity in, 139
Magellan, 145
man: origin of, 135f.; relation to God,
managerial class, 177
Marduk, 29, 30, 37f., 50
Mars, motion of, 102
martyr(s), 51; Galileo as, 107f.
Marx, Karl, 154, 173, 175ff.
Marxism: anti-religious teaching of, 173; and dogma, 154
mathematics: Descartes and, 113ff.; and form, 68ff.; Galileo and, 104; Plato and, 70ff.; subject of, 69
matter: Cartesian view, 113ff.; conservation of, 149; creation of, 148f.; and evil, 76; and forms, 76, 130
meaning, 137
mechanics, celestial, 103
Messiah, hope, of, 80
metaphysics, Aristotle and, 130
Middle Ages: and reform movements, 91; tradition and, 88f.
millennium, 170, 175; *see also* chiliasm
mind, and matter, 137f.
minds, intercommunication, 138
miracles, 14f.
monasticism, 84
monotheism, Jewish, 49
moon, 96
morality, *see* ethics
mortality, and evolution, 134
Moses, 47, 48, 86
motion: absolute, 122; laws of, 117f.; relative, 98f.
mutations, biological, 133, 134
myth(s): and Christianity, 78; cosmogonical, 25, 26ff.; migration of, 34; and philosophy, 34ff.; physical interpretation of, 41; Plato's, 73; psychological interpretation, 38ff.
mythos: and *logos*, 26, 55; meaning, 27; Plato's use of, 73

Napoleon, 25
nature, 92, 120; gods and, 37f.; *see also* laws of nature
Nebuchadnezzar, 47
nebulae, 124, 143f.; spiral, 124, 144
necessity, 75, 124f.
neo-Platonism, 85
Nernst, Walther, 151ff.
Neumann, J. von, 139
New Testament, 83, 85
Newton, Isaac, 22, 24, 103, 105, 113, 115, 117ff., 122, 132
Nippur, 38
Noah, 50
nominalism, 90
non-being, existence of, 62
Nudimuned, 28

obedience, 93
Occam's razor, 96, 100, 134, 136
Odin, 32, 50
Okeanos, 39, 55

Index

Old Testament, 25f., 27, 49; and creation, 42f., 126
Olympians, 31
ontology, 56
opinion, and truth, 59, 69

pacifism, and early Christians, 82f.
Parmenides, 57ff., 69
Pascal, Blaise, 52
Pauli, W., 136
Pavlov, I. P., 23
peace: ambivalence of, 83; enforcement of, 19
phenomena, saving the, 97, 100, 104
phenomenology, 131
philosophy: Christianity and, 85ff.; and myth, 34ff.; and theology, distinction, 88f.
physics; as science, 14f.; and life, 137f.
planets, 22, 96ff., 113f., 117f.; outside solar system, 144
planning, 20
Plato, 60, 66ff., 106, 122, 125; *Republic*, 72, 73; *Timaeus*, 25, 27, 66f., 70, 73, 85
poetry, and myth, 33
political responsibility, and Christianity, 82f.
politics, and secularization, 164
Polo, Marco, 145
polonium, 142
Pope: at Avignon, 91; and Emperor, contest, 91
population, increase of, 18
potentia, 132
Priestly Code, 46
priests, and truth, 15f.
progress, belief in, 171f.
Prometheus, 31
propaganda, dangers of, 21
Prophets, 47f.
proteins, 135
psychogony, 38
Ptolemy of Alexandria, 95, 98ff.
Pythagoreans, 26

Quakers, 171
quantum theory, 61

radiation, solar and stellar, 146
radium, 142
Raphael, 89
realism, Thomist, 90
reality, 90ff., 120f.
reason: and natural law, 125; and revelation, 89; sufficient, principle of, 123
red shift, 147f., 151
reflexes, conditioned, 23
Reformation, 166
relativism, historical, 173f.
religion: atheistic, 4, 22; and experience, 77f.; faith in science as, 12f.; indispensable elements of, 13
resurrection of the body, 153
revolution(s), 164ff.; ambivalence of, 168, 177; American, 164, 177; astronomical, 101; and Christianity, 169; English, 164, 177; French, 94, 165, 177; Russian, 164
ritual: and religion, 16; technical, 17
Roman Empire, and Christianity, 82f., 112
Rousseau, J.-J., 177
Russia, 13

Santillana, G. de, 109

science: modern, relation to Christianity, 163; philosophical background of, 181; as substitute for religion, 13f.; and technology, 11f.; trustworthiness of, 14; truth of, 11; universality of, 14f.
scientism, 13, 15; ambiguity of, 21f.; arguments against, 18ff.; and dogmas of infinity, 151ff.; dogmatism of, 154; success of, 18; as unconscious philosophy, 61
Second Coming, Christ's, 169f.
sects, Protestant, 171
secularization, 94, 126, 159, 160ff., 178ff.; criticism, of, 162; as heresy, 179; significance of, 162
selection, natural, 133f.
selection pressure, 134
self-control, 165
separation, 48, 81
Sermon on the Mount, 80, 82, 170
servitude, basis of, 20
Socrates, 70
solar system, movement of, 94ff.
soul, 40
sovereignty, national, 19
space: absolute, 121f.; atomism and, 62f.; cosmic, 145; curvature of, 145, 147; distribution of objects in, 143f.; in Greek thought, 122; infinite, 149
species: and form, 130; origin of, 127f.
spheres, harmony of the, 102
Spirit, 52
Spirituals, Franciscan, 171
spring, annual victory of, 37, 41
stars: age of, 147; fixed, distance of, 100; formation of, 147; motions of, 95ff.
State, development of, 91, 93
subconscious mind, 21, 38f.
success, ambivalence of, 177f.
sun: age of, 151; constitution of, 143f.; and earth, relative motion, 94ff.; radiation of, 146

technology, and science, relation, 11f.
tehom, 46
Thales, 54ff., 59
theology: metaphysical, 52f.; and philosophy, distinction, 89
therapy, *see* diagnosis
thermodynamics, second law of, 150, 152
Thirty Years' War, 109
Thomas Aquinas, St, 88, 90
Tiâmat, 27ff., 37, 38, 39, 46, 55
time: absolute, 122; Augustine on, 87; beginning of, 148f.; Christianity and, 155f.; cosmic, 146f.; first, 36; infinite duration of, 148, 149, 151ff.; lack of, 21
Titans, 31
Torricelli, 105
totalitarianism, Church and, 109
transcendence, 88
Trent, Council of, 109
trust, meaning of term, 14
truth, priests and, 15; *see also* opinion

universe: age of, 146ff.; beginning in time, 150, 152f., 155f.; expanding, 147; infinity of, 65, 151f.
uranium, 142

vacuum, 105
Ve, 32
Vili, 32
void, the, 63
vortices, 113f.

war, abolition of, 19
water, 37, 39, 54ff., 59
Whitehead, A. N., 11
world, beginning of, *see* beginning; universe

Yahve, 47, 49, 50
yawning, 36
Ymir, 31f., 37

Zeus, 31, 37, 50
zodiac, 97, 114, 144